Haircutting for Everyone

Haircutting for Everyone

Harold Leighton

Photography Bill Ling
Make-up Celia Hunter and Sara

Arthur Barker Limited, London
A subsidiary of Weidenfeld (Publishers) Limited

To Maxine, Philip and Adam,
twenty years later – my love always

My grateful thanks are due to photographer Bill Ling,
for his sensitive treatment of the subject,
and to Sally Voak, who translated my garbled English into
something more intelligible

Copyright © Harold Leighton 1977

Published in Great Britain in 1977 by Arthur Barker Limited,
91 Clapham High Street, London SW4 7TA

Reprinted June 1980

Editor Maureen Waller
Designer Sandra Shafee
Cased edition ISBN 0 213 16654 2
Paperback edition ISBN 213 16659 3

Printed in Great Britain by
Fletcher & Son Limited, Norwich, Norfolk

Contents

1 You and Your Hair

For the last twenty years, I've been intimately concerned with *hair* — which is probably why I haven't got much of my own! Haircutting, styling, shampooing, conditioning, colouring — every single aspect of hair care. I've learnt on my travels all over the world that hair is the barometer of good health, and an important confidence-builder. If your hair looks good, you feel good. Its condition, texture and shine are three vital clues to the general health and vitality of the individual.

Because hair is so important, most people want their hair, cut and condition, to be in tip top shape all the time. Of course, the lucky few can afford to spend time and money making sure it is just that. But, for most people, it just isn't possible to visit the hairdresser's salon every week. That is why I've written this book.

I feel strongly that there is no substitute for the expertise and care of a good hairdresser — after all, I'm one myself. But I also feel that men and women should be able to care for their hair themselves between visits to the hairdresser. They should know how to shampoo, condition and even occasionally, cut, their own hair. They should be able to use the gadgets and products available to get the best results, and to know how to select the treatments, shampoos and equipment that are right for their hair. They should also be able to adapt and ring the changes with their basic style. To understand, and cope with, the hair problems that result from pollution, air-conditioning, stress and other problems of the twentieth-century environment.

As a working, globe-trotting hairdresser, I'm in a unique position to pass on the tips of the trade and the benefit of my experience.

I've worked with hard-pressed businessmen, leading models, film stars and actresses, working mothers, socialites, housewives and harassed husbands, wriggling children, long-haired teenagers.

I know what can happen to basically good hair under the combined stress of a bad perm, heavy-handed shampooing, harsh colouring. I've had to sort out many, many problems like this.

I know that most mothers want their children's hair to look neat and well-groomed and yet haven't the time, opportunity or cash to take them to the hairdresser's very often. And I've seen some of the disasters and 'pudding basin' styles that result from badly-cut home hair-dos.

I know what it's like to rush home from work with hair looking dull and lank and just half an hour to get ready for an important outing. I know what to do about it, too.

I know how tempting it is to switch your hair-colour around to suit your mood or the current fashion — and how disastrous it can be for your hair's condition.

Luckily, hairdressing and hair products have both made tremendous advances over the past five years. With the help of the magazines that write about hair care, and the high standards set by the big international hairdressing chains, the accent is now well and truly on hair *health* as well as fashionable styling.

I believe that you should be your own hair health watchdog. You should know your own hair type, growth pattern and how your hair is likely to react under certain conditions. In hot sunlight, in a centrally-heated atmosphere, in damp weather. You should also know when it's necessary to bring in professional trichological advice. It seems to me to be unreasonable to march in 'cold' to a new hairdresser and expect him or her to work miracles without some basic information from the client. And yet, people do it all the time.

So, in this book, I'm aiming to arm potential hairdressing clients with some good, basic knowledge about their own hair type and problems.

Read it – and then discover the hairdresser who'll work wonders with your hair. I guarantee that the results will be far more satisfactory from both sides.

Finally, remember that this is a very personal book put together by a close team of hairworking, hair-conscious friends. Hope it gets to the roots of your hair hang-ups.

2 Me and My Hair

I asked some of my friends in the fashion and beauty world to write a few words about just what their hair means to them, and how important it is in their professional lives:

Paulene Stone has been a top international model for several years. She's a beautiful natural redhead whose striking colouring is one of the most important factors behind her success. She says: 'If my hair looks right, then I feel right. Like all models, I have to be able to cope with my hair myself between visits to top crimpers like my good friend Harold. If only I'd had a book like this one when I first started modelling, I could have saved myself a lot of worry and armache. For I had to learn to understand my hair the hard way – by making lots of mistakes. I now wear my hair mid-long, have it cut every few months and wash it and blow it dry or set it on heated rollers myself.

'I've styled it into "casual" glamour on scorching beaches, in telephone boxes, tiny hotel rooms, jungle clearings, on top of mountains – you name it. Believe me, behind those glossy magazine pictures lies an awful lot of preparation, in far from glamorous conditions.

'Every model girl's dream would be to have someone like Harold as a permanent shadow to work wonders with her hair wherever she happens to be working.

'This book seems to me to be the next best thing!'

Shirley Conran is a leading magazine and newspaper editor and the successful author of *Superwoman*, a marvellous 'how to' manual for every hardpressed mum and career girl. She says: 'I think that most women get into a tizz about their hair if it doesn't look good. I know that I do. That's why I cheat a bit by relying on hair-pieces and wigs to give my own fine hair a glamorous look, and to save time and money at the hairdresser's. If you feel confident about your appearance, then everything seems to go much better.

'I'm not the only professional lady with a highly developed hair sense, either. Margaret Thatcher gets up extra early several mornings a week for a professional "comb-out"; you never see Barbara Castle with a single hair out of place; Angela Rippon always looks beautifully groomed; Esther Rantzen actually wears heated rollers during the final run-through of her TV show, just so that her hair looks perfect on the screen.

'We're all going to learn a lot from this book, Harold. Good-looking hair is one of the few things that you can achieve with a little well-spent money and common sense.'

Eliza Kendall writes about Health for *Vogue* magazine. She says: 'To me, hair is part of the whole health and beauty spectrum – and I'm delighted that *condition* is now such an important factor with hairdressers, including you, Harold. Understanding how hair relates to nutrition and bodily processes is the first step towards possessing a swinging, shining healthy head of hair. These days, young people are becoming more aware of this – and your book can really help educate them still more.

'Fashion is an ever-changing process, and naturally most youngsters want to keep up with the latest hair fashions. Fine, so long as their hair can stand it! I've learnt that a basic, fairly short cut suits me and I keep it in tip top condition between visits to my hairdresser with a mild shampoo and gentle conditioner; and I like to let it dry naturally.

'I think your book is excellent, Harold – and I wish you good luck with it.'

Andree Grenfell is President of Glemby International Europe. She says: 'I feel I know Harold very well (being his boss) and I know we share the same feelings about how hair should look and feel. I believe that well-cut hair is the secret of easy-to-manage hair and because of my job it is obviously essential that my hair *always* looks its best.

'I have it cut professionally every six weeks and I wash it at home at least three times a week. I also have a conditioning treatment once a week in the salon to keep the shine and condition in top form.

'I am fortunate in that I have found a hairdresser who really understands me and my hair and who cuts it in such a way that I know it will always fall into place and look good.'

3 All About Your Hair

How's your hair *condition*? Is it shiny, sexy, swinging? If not, why not?

Before you even think about cutting, setting or blowing your hair dry yourself, it makes sense to know something about the way your hair grows, what it's made of and the conditions needed to help it stay healthy.

Hair is the body's 'barometer', indicating good health or lack of it, rather like a dog's coat. If you've ever had a bad cold and noticed that your hair looked dull and messy, you will have been reading this 'barometer' yourself. If you've ever returned from holiday and been delighted by the shiny, manageable condition of your hair, you'll have been taking another 'reading', without even considering that your whole body was registering 'all systems go'. As a hairdresser used to handling regular clients' hair each week, I know that the hair 'barometer' can swing up and down disconcertingly rapidly — drugs, hormonal changes, weather changes, a different environment and emotional disturbances can all play their part in changing hair colour, condition and even texture. Women on the Pill often find that their hair becomes greasier, dryer or different in texture (sometimes much easier to handle) according to the way hormones contained in the Pill affect their bodies.

However, with care and foresight you and your hairdresser can cope with these hair 'moods'. First, you must know something about it:

What is hair?

If you chopped a single hair in half, then magnified the cut end under a very powerful microscope, you'd see that hair has a distinct core or shaft and this core is surrounded by what look like overlapping roof tiles. These tiles are sleek looking when they lie flat, but can be disturbed if pieces of dirt or grit get lodged underneath them — too much harsh treatment can chip bits of 'tile' off or make the whole hair split in two. That's why I, and most other condition-conscious hairdressers, recommend regular, gentle washing to dislodge potentially harmful 'foreign bodies'. It's a myth that too much washing makes hair more greasy.

The hair itself is made from a type of protein called 'keratin', the same ingredient that makes up your toe- and finger-nails and your eyelashes. Some conditioning treatments these days can actually penetrate the hair shaft and renew protein supplies from within the hair. But the best way to make sure your hair gets a regular supply is to *eat* it. (See my hair-care diet on page 15.)

How does it grow?

Each hair grows from a snug cavity called the hair 'follicle'. Each follicle is quite a deep little hole in your scalp — honestly! If you pluck out one hair and look at it very closely, you'll see that it has a slightly bulbous shaped root, with traces of blood on it. The hair is fed by an efficient blood-flow to the hair follicle, which is why good circulation is so vital for healthy hair and also why some

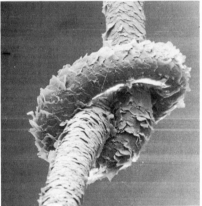

1 A highly magnified shot of a healthy undamaged hair illustrating how the layers of cuticle remain firmly bonded together, and 2 a damaged hair where the layers of the cuticle have separated which means the hair will split easily.
Photographs by courtesy of Wella International.

kinds of baldness can be helped by scalp stimulation and massage. Your hair grows at the rate of about half an inch a month – six inches a year – but it also grows at slightly different rates all over the head, which is why that super cut can go out of shape and become uneven if it's not attended to regularly. This growth-rate means that the ends of long hair are ancient. A girl or guy with eighteen-inch hair has three-year-old hair ends. No wonder long hair so often looks tatty. Some people have such fine or delicate hair that it just won't grow that long - not because it's not being fed from the root, but because the ends keep breaking off. This type of hair needs regular cutting to keep it looking good and really isn't successful worn long.

What makes it shiny?

Sebum, excreted by the sebaceous glands situated half-way up the hair follicle, is often blamed for greasy hair conditions. True, over-active sebaceous glands are the nasties that cause greasy hair, but they're made that way by hormonal activity in the body. Sebum in the right quantities is really a beneficent agent, giving shine and lustre to your hair. It's a natural lubricant and protective fluid that keeps your hair bouncy in different weather conditions. Obviously in sunshine the sebum is dried up giving you that midsummer 'haystack' look. Ideally, sebum should flow down the full length of the hair shaft. But sometimes this may be prevented by dandruff encrustations on the surface of the scalp or dirt. Dry ends are caused simply by the fact that the sebum has run out of steam before reaching the ends. If your hair follicles tend to produce only a small amount of sebum, then your only solution may be to wear your hair shorter or to try a diet which contains more oily foods.

Shine can also be produced by 'coating' the hair shaft with a colourant or conditioning cream, building up a little extra thickness and lustre artificially. Many people find their hair looks shinier and thicker with highlights or a colourant which is just a shade or two different from their natural colour.

Why does it fall out?

Hair falls out all the time – a hundred or more hairs in a single day. But new hairs are also growing all the time, if your scalp is healthy, so that you hair does not become noticeably thinner. Exceptions to this for women can be just after having a baby or even during pregnancy itself (though most women find that their hair looks extra-good during pregnancy – one of nature's 'presents' to future mums). The hair lost after childbirth, however, is quickly replaced if the woman goes on a healthy, high-protein diet and looks after herself properly. Some women find that their bodies simulate the post-pregnant state during the period after they come off the Pill and their hair falls out then, but it certainly does grow again. But what turns so many men into baldies? Stress and heredity is closely related to the hormonal activities that cause excessive hair fall-out in men – and these days more women are experiencing alopecia (baldness) because of stress. Other causes can be bad hair treatment – perm upon perm causing breakage, over-bleaching, incorrectly applied strong colourants. Hair transplants may work well for some, but they are expensive and should only be undertaken by experts. (How to find one? Best to consult your local scalp hospital or consultant trichologist – look for trichologists who are Members of the Institute of Trichologists.) Remember, hair transplanting is surgery, and should not be regarded as anything other than that.

What makes it colourful, curly or straight?

Blame genes for your hair colour – if both parents are dark, then you are likely to be dark too, if one is fair and the other is ginger, then the gingery gene is likely to predominate. Heredity is the main factor in hair colour. Genes, too, decide whether your hair will be curly or straight, and by the way, those curls are actually made that way *below* the surface of the scalp within the hair follicle. I'm not in favour of the hair straightening processes available now, simply because 'reverse perming' has to be harsh to work at all and breakage can follow all too easily. But nowadays, hair colouring techniques are really super – there's no need for harsh treatment unless a radical change is wanted, and as a strong believer that nature usually needs *help*, not knocking for six, it should not be necessary to torture your hair to change its colour. Home colour changes can be tricky, though, usually because people just don't read the instructions on the colourant label or leaflet enclosed with the product.

If it's any comfort, some hairdressers aren't above the occasional disaster either – 'correction' jobs are very common in hairdressing salons. Unfortunately, it often takes two or three visits before badly-coloured hair can return to a good tone and condition, so that if your hair needs 'correcting' be patient with the hairdresser you choose to do it for you.

The five types of colouring product

Temporary colourants These give extra depth or interesting highlights to the natural hair colour. They wash off with the next shampoo. They colour the surface of the hair shaft only. Although a wide range of colours is available you can really only successfully intensify or slightly darken your natural hair colour with a temporary colourant. If you have brown hair, for instance, you could achieve reddish lights or perhaps a slightly deeper brown. If your hair is very porous (through over-bleaching or exposure to the sun on holiday), there may be a slight colour build-up from one application to the next. If the porous bit is at the ends of the hair, this colour pile-up will often happen right at the very ends giving an uneven look. Manufacturers cannot make these colourants any more intense, simply because more colour would just rub off or cause the scalp to become stained. Some hairdressers use a type of temporary colourant incorporated into a setting lotion – this will simply tone the hair or add blueish or pinkish tints to grey or very fair hair. Used each week this could cause colour build-up.

Traditional semi-permanents These intensify the natural colour or make a slight change of up to two or three shades – always darker. They can't make the hair colour lighter (to do that, a colourant incorporating a bleach must be used). Here's what happens when you, or your hairdresser, applies one of these products: the direct dyes in the product penetrate the cuticle part of the hair shaft and deposit colour just inside the 'cortex' which is the colour layer of the hair, where it stays just beside the natural colour. The two mingle, but the natural hair colour isn't removed. Re-growth usually presents no problem, since the colourant fades from shampoo to shampoo anyway, so that the 'tide mark' becomes fainter and fainter. Be warned that a strong semi-permanent colour such as red (especially applied to a porous, light coloured hair) could leave a mark and cause colour build-up problems. If you're doing a colour job yourself with one of these products, do check the manufacturer's notes on the pack. Check whether they claim a lasting period measured in weeks, or in shampoos! After all, if you wash your hair every day and the product manufacturer gives a life expectancy of six to eight shampoos, you can hardly expect the colour to last six weeks. Application: most traditional semi-permanents are shampooed into towel-dried or wet hair, allowed to take for a set time, then rinsed off. Do make sure that you rinse your hair properly, otherwise you'll get a tacky-feeling result.

Stronger semi-permanents These contain oxidation dyes, which can penetrate the cortex further than the traditional semi-permanent dyes. This means that a much more radical colour change can be achieved. The usual oxidation agent used is hydrogen peroxide but the action is much weaker than that used by the peroxide in a permanent tint, so that root re-touching isn't always necessary. Most home-used products in this group will darken and shine only mouse to golden-brown, light brown through to dark brown hair. When you're choosing one, make sure that you read all the packet notes fully before you buy. If you're using a semi-permanent for the first time, aim to put interesting sheen and highlights in your hair, as often a very dark colour on light brown hair or curly hair which does not throw off a shine will have a flat-looking effect. I always advise women to avoid the very dark home dyes because they can give an ageing appearance. Stock up on old towels and strip off before you apply that home hair colourant - drip over the bath! Do leave it on for the full time indicated on the packet. And, most important, if it *says* do a strand test – *do* one! Don't forget your skin test, either.

Permanent colourants Here's where I feel strongly that the salon hairdresser is the best person to cope with your colour. For a start, he's got all the equipment needed and has years of experience to guide him. Again, these dyes penetrate the cortex with oxidation dyes but with a much, much stronger action than the semi-permanents. Your colour change will last until it grows out, although colours tend to fade a little in the summer. Many of these colourants are embodied in the shampoo – the product is applied first to the roots, then shampooed in all over and 'buffers' in the formula prevent colour build-up. Some need to be brushed onto the root, then left for a while, and brushed or combed through the rest of the hair. If you want a radical change – dark hair taken up to blonde, for instance – then your hair will have to be pre-lightened before the tint or toner is applied.

Colouring, I feel, is one of the really exciting aspects of hairdressing now. No hair remains the same colour all the time, anyway. Those 'buffers' have removed a lot of the difficulty of applying colour, and the colours available to the hairdresser are much more subtle these days. You should have a really good hairdresser for your colour-application – and make sure he or she is fully informed about the *condition* of your hair before applying colour. Over-permed or sun-bleached hair may react badly to some colourants, and it's true that the post-natal period may be dodgy for some colour treatments.

Lighteners If you want some sunshine in your hair, then you may decide to do a lightening or streaking job at home. Take care when you're choosing a product – some contain a built-in toner to bring your hair down to the shade you want, others do not. Many lightening products are 'twinned' with toners which must be applied after the lightener. Frankly, I think a salon is the best place to go for hair-lightening, unless you have the kind of hair that goes prettily fair in sunshine in summer and just needs a bit of help in winter to achieve the same look (you probably don't even need a toner, just a blonding agent). Manufacturers say that no one should try to lighten her hair more than six shades, but I think that is a bit extreme, even in a salon.

If you are doing a home job, you'll need to look at the pack carefully – note whether it's a 'gentle' lightener (one to two shades lighter), or a 'medium' lightener (four shades lighter). A 'maximum' product goes as far as you let it, depending on your natural hair colour.

You must do a strand test before lightening your hair at home. Be especially careful if your hair is porous – snip two bits of hair, one from the porous top hair, the other from the underneath hair to see the difference in colour with the same lightener! If it goes brassy looking, then you may have chosen the wrong toner. Do be careful, and if you're not sure about a colour or tone, don't do it!

I have known women who can streak or tip their own hair, but not many. Steaking should be subtle – and it's really impossible to do this yourself. If you can get a friend to help, then you may have more success. Again, I would recommend this at home only for women with naturally light or soft mousy hair. The classic method of streaking hair is to place a polythene cap on your head, then yank through the strands which are to be lightened with a crochet hook. But these must be very thin sections and they must be pulled tightly enough to ensure that the root hair isn't lightened too much because the roots take quicker than the ends – all very tricky. If you want to lighten the tips of your fringe, you could do so by applying tape (see the taped fringe on page 27) across the fringe and lightening the bottom ends only.

4 Your Hair and Your Diet

When I see clients with out-of-condition hair, one of the first questions I ask them is about their diet. Is the pace of their life making them take snatched meals? Are they getting enough protein, and enough Vitamin B? Hair is made from protein, so that naturally it is an essential part of our diet in order to grow healthy hair. Lean meat, fish, eggs, cottage cheese – they're all good hair health foods. I also recommend cutting down too many animal fats (butter, fatty meat, cream) if the hair is excessively greasy. It's healthier, anyway, to replace animal fats with vegetable oils, where possible. 'Fry-ups' every night are bound to result in over-active sebaceous glands – spottiness, and greasy hair.

What about Vitamin B? Well, trichologists have found that increasing the intake of this important vitamin group does help to improve the condition of their patients' hair. Yeast tablets are a good source, as are liver and wheatgerm. Interestingly, it's often the clients who are 'into' healthy eating – the model girls and young actresses, particularly – who have the glossiest, thickest hair, which must prove something. My own problem? I blame it on heredity and hormones – but I have the glossiest beard in town.

Here's a diet plan that's very similar to those followed by my most hair-health conscious clients. It's one I recommend to anyone who feels that her hair could look and behave a lot better than it does at present:

Every day ½ pint milk, to be used in tea or coffee. No sugar allowed – if you have a sweet tooth, use a sugar-substitute instead. 4 brewer's yeast tablets (available from most chemists), to be taken after each meal and last thing at night.

Breakfast Large glass orange juice (unsweetened); 1 egg, cooked any way; 1 slice wholemeal bread and butter; tea or coffee with milk from allowance.

Lunch Large mixed salad using seasonal vegetables (grated carrot, cabbage, cauliflower sprigs, cucumber, watercress), dressed with vegetable oil and lemon juice. Serve with a portion of fish: grilled, steamed or baked; choose white fish, shellfish, or oily fish such as mackerel. If you're at a restaurant pick the simplest fish dish on the menu. Fresh fruit salad; tea or coffee; glass of red wine, if you like (contains iron).

Supper Any lean meat (choose liver, kidney or sweetbreads twice a week) with 2 leafy, green vegetables; 1 slice wholemeal bread and butter; vegetable juice with wheatgerm and lemon juice stirred in; yoghurt or piece of fresh fruit; tea or coffee; glass of red wine, if you like.

During the day sip water or fruit juice. Try not to overload your system with endless cups of coffee.

5 Top Ten Condition Tips

It pays to have some expertise when it comes to keeping your hair in superb condition. Here are some bright ideas gleaned from my own hairdressing experience:

1 If a patch of dandruff appears (it can happen to anyone – often when you're overtired, have been eating badly or feel run down), massage your scalp for five to ten minutes and then comb through with a fine tooth comb. This will loosen the flakes before shampooing. Afterwards, rinse extra thoroughly to get rid of the loosened dandruff.

2 Always use a reliable shampoo and balance it with the correct conditioner. You'll find that these are just as varied as shampoos. You'll also find that your hair will change periodically and you may need a different shampoo. Don't go on relentlessly using a dry hair shampoo if your hair is going through a 'greasy' patch.

3 Always make sure your hair is thoroughly clean before you set it or blow it dry. Otherwise, your hair will be heavy and become sticky very quickly indeed. Remember to rinse conditioner out very thoroughly before styling.

4 Never shampoo in a hurry. If your hair is very greasy, apply the shampoo before damping with water.

5 If you have long hair, put the conditioner on the ends, spread half-way up the hair shaft only. Comb through and then rinse thoroughly. If you have bleached or very thick, long hair prone to tangles, do leave a fraction of a cream rinse in to make it easier to handle. Never pull on long hair while it's wet – it behaves just like elastic and will snap easily. When choosing a conditioner, remember that a conditioner containing balsam or protein is really meant to 'feed' the hair – it could make greasy hair over-greasy. One old remedy for greasiness is to squeeze a lemon over the hair or use a tablespoonful of vinegar in the rinsing water.

6 Cover heated roller spikes with tissue – loo paper will do. This will prevent tangles, split ends and frantic panics when you try to remove them. It will also keep the rollers clean – change the paper every week. Roll up the hair cleanly to prevent kinks. Don't exert too much pressure as you wind up unless you want a tight curl. For lank hair, use a lot of rollers in small sections and spray with a blow-drying lotion or slight setting spray after winding. Don't use a heavy setting lotion before winding.

7 Make up your own mind about the usefulness of hair spray. But don't rely on it for rigid setting. This looks old-fashioned and is bad for the hair. Hair that's well-shaped and moves about looks sexier and prettier.

8 On holiday, cover bleached, damaged, tinted or porous hair with a pretty scarf or hat. It isn't worth allowing it to become damaged – after all you'll have to live with the consequences for the rest of the year. Always wash chlorine or

sea water out of your hair after bathing.

9 Have your hair cut every six weeks – even if you're growing it longer. If you can't afford a six-weekly cut, do the job yourself and save up for a good cut later. But don't let those ends hang around splitting away!

10 Be changeable. Let your husband, wife, lover or friend see you in different ways over the years – a new hairstyle is a refreshing change for everyone. If you're still wearing the same hair-do as you did five years ago you definitely need a change.

6 How to Shampoo Your Hair

Are you *washing* your hair correctly? It's surprising how many people just don't know how to wash their own hair. Instead of treating it with the same amount of respect and care as they would their face or body, they scrub it, rub it and generally bash it around before exposing it to the full blast of a hair dryer held one-tenth of an inch away from the roots.

And men, confess – how many of you wash your hair with carbolic soap under the shower? Or, even nastier, with liquid detergent. I know several good-looking guys who take great care with their shaving technique, use the best bath-time skin lotions and are downright snobbish about cologne – but they wash their hair in a communal bath-tub each week, shared by fourteen other members of the local rugby team. No wonder they say they suffer from dandruff – it's probably grit from the pitch.

Hair is delicate, growing stuff, and it deserves gentle handling. If you work in a centrally-heated office, live in town and have a tendency to oiliness, then you're going to have to wash your hair frequently. Washing with a gentle shampoo will not make it greasier still – what will make it greasy is lots of rubbing and scrubbing on the scalp to stimulate those already far-too-active sebaceous glands.

My shampoo guide for all types of hair

Normal hair So, who's normal? Well, if your hair doesn't go greasy quickly and is fairly well-behaved and you don't have dandruff, then you could say your hair was normal. Wash it once or twice a week with a mild shampoo.

Many of the shampoos on the market contain harsh detergents which make a lot of froth and perfumes which smell divine. Never judge a shampoo by suds and smell – judge it by the way it *leaves* your hair. Manufacturers insist that the first thing people want from shampoo is lots of lather and a luscious scent. Start judging shampoo by *results*. You can still have a sensuous experience (psychologists say that self-grooming is an essential outlet for our latent narcissistic tendencies – in other words, we enjoy it) with slightly less lather and a subtler smell.

Apply just a little shampoo, work it carefully into the scalp area (don't scrub) and lightly into the ends of the hair. Logically, the ends are less grubby than the roots, and they may be much dryer and slightly porous – treat them kindly. Rinse and re-apply. You don't have to shampoo twice if it suits you not to – and if you enjoy shampooing under the shower every few days, then it's not necessary.

Conditioner? If your hair needs it to hold a style, then use a mild conditioner.

Towel-dry lightly (without rubbing – wet hair *stretches*), comb through, then set or blow dry – holding the dryer at least six inches away from the hair. Harsh drying really will strip sebum from your good-tempered 'normal' hair and make it act up alarmingly. Why risk it?

Greasy hair The most common problem among my customers is the one of greasy hair. Stress can be partly blamed for this as can hormonal activity (particularly during puberty, teens and after childbirth) and poor thyroid function. Try to calm down and eat sensibly (avoiding fatty foods and chocolate) if you have this problem – but do wash your hair carefully just before it starts to become 'tacky'. If you leave it greasy, then it won't just look terrible, but dirt and grit specks could stick to the grease, get lodged under the overlapping scales on the hair's surface and cause breakage and damage. The grease will also encourage dandruff and poor skin condition on face, neck and back. Use a lemon or other greasy hair shampoo, working well into the scalp before lathering your whole head. Try to use the shower attachment on the bath or the shower itself for rinsing so that you can be sure to get rid of *all* the grease and dirt, and the shampoo itself when you rinse. If you like, add vinegar or lemon juice to the final rinsing water to leave it squeaky-clean.

Try to choose a simple style (like one of the styles in this book) which enables you to wash your hair and set or blow-dry it at home. Clean, shiny hair looks great cut very simply and greasy hair often has plenty of natural 'body'. Some of my clients find that a colourant or light perm takes away some of that greasiness – a good idea if you don't have time to shampoo every few days.

You probably won't need a conditioner every wash – perhaps once or twice a month only. Towel-dry, comb through and set or blow-dry in the usual way. *What about dry shampoos?* Use one if you're desperate and just have to go out on a special date when there's no time to wash. But do make sure that you follow the directions recommended on the product – those white bits look very much like dandruff if they're not brushed out properly.

Dry hair Wash once or twice a week with a creamy shampoo, and use a good conditioning treatment afterwards. Rinse the conditioner off very thoroughly to avoid stickiness. Be really gentle with the ends of your hair, which are probably the dryest part. If the scalp is very dry and flaky, you need an anti-dandruff shampoo. If the trouble persists, consult your hairdresser or a trichologist. Try the following treatment every two weeks: use henna wax and wrap cling film or a warmed towel around your head; leave it on for half an hour, then rinse thoroughly and shampoo in the normal way.

Watch out for the temptation of using strong hair spray to tame dry or fly-away hair, as this could just aggravate the condition and make your hair dull and lifeless. Your main problem is an inadequate flow of sebum from the roots of your hair – dandruff may be causing a scalp encrustation which is preventing the shine service from getting through. Once you've tackled that little problem, concentrate on stimulating the circulation and the sebum flow with a scalp massage: cup hands with fingers a little apart and press the pads of your fingertips onto the scalp. Pressing gently, make circular movements without moving your fingertips. Now place the fingers on a different part of your scalp and repeat the process all over your head. This feels delicious if someone else is doing it too. I recommend this just before shampooing.

Children's hair It's a great pity that so many children hate having their hair washed. Many mums dread shampoo nights for this reason. I think shampooing can be fun. First, bring up baby to enjoy having his or her hair washed and scalp gently massaged – you can't start too young. You can tuck the child firmly under one arm as you rinse his head with lukewarm water in a bath or bowl. Make sure the water doesn't go into the eyes by using a Halo Cap from the chemist – if he distrusts his hairstylist now, he could grow up with a permanent anti-hairdresser complex. Wrap the child up in a warm, fluffy towel and make the whole experience a pleasant one.

Later, it's fun for children to pretend that they're at a real hairdresser's salon. Sit each of them up on a chair in style to wash their hair and use a 'no-tears' baby shampoo, rubbed in very gently. Most children have non-greasy hair (puberty brings those greasy, spotty changes), so that one shampoo only will be sufficient. If you like to wash their hair in the bath, make sure the water doesn't contain any harsh detergent-based bubble bath which could harm their hair as they dive under. Always rinse with the bath shower attachment or under the shower. Britmarine swim goggles are handy here – and make the whole operation even more fun.

Wrap their hair, turban-style, in a towel, sit each child on a chair and blow-dry. Let them style each other's hair if you have several children. If not, why not try a family hair-do night once a week? If a cut or trim is necessary (particularly that first professional cut), then take your child along to the hairdresser's salon with you for one visit before his or her own 'turn' – just to see exactly what's involved and who all the people are.

Nowadays, most salons are friendly places, so that the old 'horror' of visiting the hairdresser's is dying out fast. It pays to invest in a good cut once in a while – and to keep things up by using the trimming techniques described in chapter 12.

7 Shampoo Guide – Step-by-Step

Are you shampooing your hair correctly? Possibly not. Most people are all froth and bubbles when it comes to shampooing – they overwash the ends of their hair, and underwash the roots. Here's how to be a super-washer:

1 Gather equipment together: shampoo, conditioner, towel, brush, comb.

2 Place towel or cape around your shoulders and brush through your hair gently to remove tangles.

3 Brush hair forward. Fill sink or bowl with hand-hot water (not red hot, please) and wet hair or, even better, spray hair with shower or spray attachment fixed onto taps.

4 Now put a little shampoo onto the back of your head, near the nape, and massage well into the *roots* of the hair, working up a little lather (not too much) as you go. Remember that suds are put in shampoos for 'fun', to make the experience nice for you – more suds don't make cleaner hair. Only put shampoo straight onto dry hair if you have a very greasy scalp or wish to remove oil or gel.

5 Allow suds and shampoo to trickle down the length of the hair and rub very gently. The ends of the hair are the cleanest as well as the most fragile part – they don't need lots of rubbing.

6 Rinse thoroughly and reapply if necessary. It is not necessary to shampoo twice if you usually wash your hair more than once a week.

7 Towel-dry hair gently, then apply conditioner if you use it. Work this into the ends, which are likely to be the dryest part and need most conditioner. If your hair tends to be oily, don't apply it at all to the roots – sebum excreted from the hair follicle will be all the natural conditioner you need. Comb through the hair very gently, leave the product on your hair for the time specified on the bottle or sachet, then rinse thoroughly.

8 Wrap your hair in a soft towel to absorb drips before blowing dry or setting.

9 Use this time to wash your brushes and combs thoroughly, adding a little antiseptic (like Dettol) to the final rinsing water.

8 How to Get the Most Out of Your Hairdresser

Most people want good service from their hairdresser, but in many cases they prevent themselves from getting just that by their daft attitude towards the hairdresser. How can he or she be expected to work miracles without some basic information from the client? With the needs of all good hairdressers very much at heart, I've compiled a list of relevant information which the customer can, and should, give her hairdresser – we're not prying, we just want to do the best job we can.

Explain why you've come Were you recommended? Did you simply pass by and feel drawn in? Did you read about the salon in a magazine or newspaper? Tell the stylist, and then he or she will know a lot more about you. For a start, he'll be able to deduce whether you can afford the kind of prices that are charged at the salon – and they may be higher than you're used to. If you give the impression that you're always visiting expensive salons you may be shattered by the bill, and really annoyed. After all, if you go along to a new doctor, your old doctor will pass on your 'case history' to him. Similarly, it helps if you're as frank as possible with your hairdresser.

Tell him all you know about your hair You'd be surprised how many women pretend that they never have their hair coloured when they go to a new hairdresser. 'It's naturally that way,' they say blithely, and then wonder why the colour lifts slightly with the first shampoo by the new stylist.

Does your hair take a set quickly? Does it hold curl? Have you had a perm recently? Has it been coloured or cut recently? All this information isn't so that we can criticize your previous hairdresser. We need to know it simply so that we can do the right job *now*.

Generally, British women are hopeless at giving this kind of information – they feel it's a sign of vanity to even pretend to know so much about themselves. Continental women have no such scruples – they're brought up to be healthily vain and to know their own good points and faults. They'll tell you all about their hair type and condition. Likewise, if they have hair that holds a set beautifully, they'll tell you about it.

Tell him what you want from your hair-do Are you a socialite who wants to look glamorous all day? Do you spend most of your time rushing around town working hard? Do you do lots of cooking? Tell your hairdresser, then your style is much more likely to turn out to be practical as well as attractive. If you've got to be able to cope with your own hairstyle between visits, say so, then you won't be landed with a complicated style that always needs professional attention.

Let him pick up your vibrations Relax and have a chat with your hairstylist, then he'll know what kind of person you are, and be able to give you a better and more practical service. Hairdressers are sensitive people, usually artistic — and if you let them, they'll do their best for you. But if you feel something isn't quite right, say so. It's amazing the number of clients who just aren't happy with the way a cut, for instance, is going who don't say a thing about it until the end of the session and *then* say it wasn't what they wanted. Don't go all stiff and moody — say something!

Relax at the hairdresser's *Use* your hairdresser for what he is — someone who's at your service to make you feel and look good. Switch off, unwind, flirt with him, confess to him, have a giggle, chat about clothes . . . just relax. You'll go out feeling refreshed as well as looking smart.

9 Hairstyling —
the Step-by-Step Way

On the following pages, you'll find a variety of real-life 'models' with the step-by-step guide to each hair-do. In some cases, the hair is cut before styling, in others I show you how to ring the changes with a basic style. I've also included a complete perm — from cut, through perming to three different looks with the finished hair-do (natural-dried, blow-dried, roller-set).

   I show you simple ways to cut children's hair, a super style for men, how to cope with long hair — everything you need to know.

   If you feel nervous about cutting your own or a friend's hair, don't worry. There are only *three* basic cuts in the book: a simple bob; a short, graduated cut; and a longer, layered cut. The bob, which is suitable for straight, fairly thick hair, is so straightforward that you can cut it yourself. Don't believe me? Turn to page 26, where you'll see a 'first-timer' cutting her own hair into an up-to-the-minute style using my easy instructions!

   Before you attempt any style, make sure you have the equipment you need — and read through the instructions several times before you start cutting or styling the hair. Keep the book open in front of you as you work, checking your technique carefully against that used in the pictures. Do work slowly!

   Hope you enjoy hairstyling as much as I do.

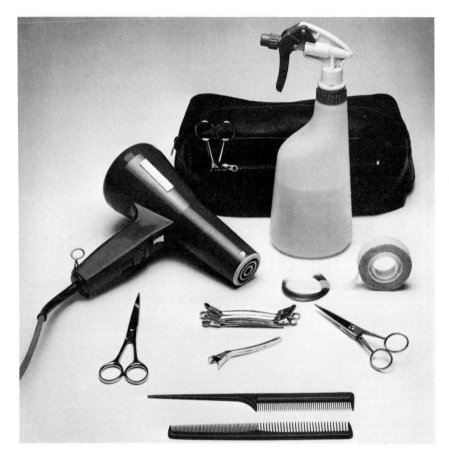

A pair of 4½″–6½″ scissors (buy special haircutting scissors obtainable from most leading stores), straight-edged comb (to use as a cutting guide) as well as a straightforward comb, water spray, hair clips, Scotch tape (not ordinary sticky tape), hand dryer (750–1000 watts, plus adaptors for use abroad, and check your plugs and have your dryer serviced periodically for safety), plastic or leather travel-bag to pack everything into.

If you want good-looking hair, you must have the right equipment. If you use a tatty brush, broken comb and heavy, old-fashioned rollers then you won't achieve a really professional-looking style. Most good hairdressers take pride in their own styling equipment (indeed, things often get a bit fraught in the salon when a leading stylist mislays his scissors): they keep scissors sharp, rollers immaculate, brushes sterilized.

You can take the same care at home. Start by checking through the hairstyling equipment you have now. Does that old brush deserve a decent burial? Could you treat yourself to a new hair dryer? Often, for the price of a new dress you can buy a whole range of equipment which will give far more glamour in the long run than any item of clothing.

If you intend to treat yourself to a new hairbrush, I recommend investing in one of my own designs. I developed two hairdressing tools several years ago which are available at large stores throughout the world. The Stylar is round and specifically for blow-styling curly, permed or straight hair. Its quills grip the hair firmly but gently so that you don't have to hold the hair around it while you style. Bounce and movement are easily formed, giving a natural look to the

style. The Stylar is easily dismantled for cleaning, and the quills withstand 1300-watt hand dryers. The Curvar is larger and curved for styling longer hair, made up of a group of separate quill sections which act like a series of combs for brushing through a set, moulding the hair into any shape or style.

Make sure all your hairstyling equipment is in prime condition — scissors super-sharp, combs and brushes perfectly clean. Keep it together in a good-looking travel-bag which will store neatly in your wardrobe or suitcase. If you leave dryer, combs and other equipment lying about, they'll become dusty and unhygienic.

11 The Simple Bob Cut

Mary is a busy career girl and mother; she works with her photographer husband, who took all the photographs in this book, in his studio just off Fleet Street, London.

She has straight hair which was cut in layers before she started her self-cut. She wants to grow it longer, so that I suggested this very simple but chic bob which would bring the layers neatly into line. She had absolutely no previous hairdressing experience before starting the cut — yet managed to do it all herself.

Fancy a smart bob like Mary's? First, make sure you have the right *type* of hair — straight, but with a fair amount of natural thickness and body. This cut is *not* suitable for curly, permed or very wispy hair.

Before you cut Shampoo your hair carefully, condition, comb through and rinse. Comb through again carefully.

You need
shampoo, conditioner
Scotch tape (don't use ordinary sticky tape)
sharp cutting scissors
comb
clips to hold wet hair
blow-styling and brushing brushes
blow-dryer
two mirrors (so that you can check the back of your hair) — a large one and a smaller hand mirror
water spray.

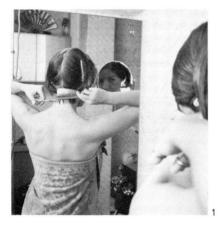

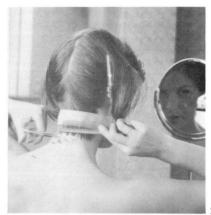

1 Make a centre parting and clip side hair up and out of the way. Make a horizontal parting 2½″ above nape and clip away hair. Now place a strip of Scotch tape just above the line you want to cut, from ear-lobe to ear-lobe around the back of your neck. Make sure the tape is perfectly positioned before you start.

2 Looking into the smaller mirror, with your back to the large one, start cutting. It's important to relax and cut little by little (the tape will hold things nicely in place), as too much hair in the scissors will make you press too hard, which is tiring and it could lead to an uneven result. Use your comb as a cutting guide.

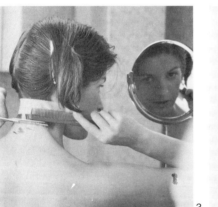

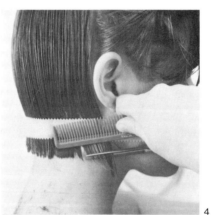

3 Carefully does it! Mary is working from left to right, but if you're left-handed you may find it easier to work from right to left. This first layer of hair is easier to cut as it's less bulky to handle. Mary's first layer was longer than the next layers, so that she had about 1½″ of hair to cut.

4 Now make another horizontal parting 2½″ above the first one. Re-tape the hair, after clipping the surplus securely out of the way. And cut again. This time, on Mary's hair, there was only around ½″ to cut to bring the hair into line. Repeat the procedure, combing down the next layer of hair, 2½″ above the previous one.

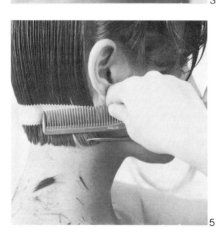

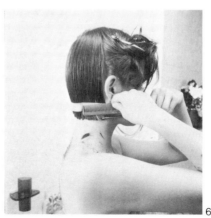

5 Because the hair is now thicker, you'll need two strips of tape for your next cut. Keep trimming carefully and evenly – take a break if your arms become tired.

6 Watch your ear-lobes – don't snip too close. Use your comb to keep the line straight and protect them.

7 Now comb down the side hair from your centre parting, and stick with double tape. Follow the same line, but make the side and front hair fractionally longer than the back. The weight of the hair is an important factor in the swinging shape.

8 Repeat with the other side of your hair. Now comb the fringe down from your parting or the crown of your head – don't go too far back on the crown, or you'll have too much fringe and not enough 'back' hair giving a front-heavy look. Scotch tape right around the fringe. If the hair has dried out a little, damp it down carefully – you can't get an even, neat line if you cut dry hair.

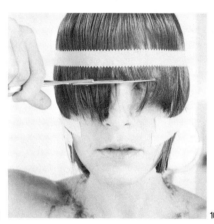

9 Start to cut just a small section in the front of your fringe, above your nose. Make it *longer* than you think you'll want the finished look. This is important: the tape is pressing the hair flat against your head – when it's blown dry the hair will be more bouncy and the fringe will look shorter. So keep that first cut way below eyebrow level.

10 Cut towards the right, again in small sections, then to the left. If you like, remove the tape at this stage, check length, then replace tape and trim away a little more. Don't forget – you can always cut away more hair from your fringe later.

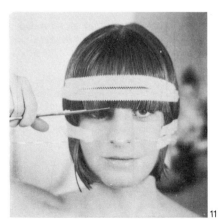

11 and 12 Satisfied with that fringe? See the length that Mary ended up with – revealing her eyes, but covering her brows.

13

14

15

16

17

18

13 Now remove the tape and towel-dry your hair before you start to blow-dry and shape it. There's absolutely no point in tiring your arms by trying to dry dripping wet hair from scratch with a blow-dryer. If you've ever been kept waiting ages in a salon by a junior struggling to blow-dry dripping hair, you'll know how unnecessary it is. Mary has straight hair and to achieve volume with her simple bob cut, it's best to blow-dry her hair and brush it forward from the nape of the neck.

14 She does this easily with her head tilted slightly forward, using my Curvar to give a smooth line.

15 Brush the sides of the hair forward in a swinging line.

16 Be gentle with the brush strokes, head hanging well down until the hair is dry. Now throw back your hair, make a centre parting and brush into shape. The forward drying method will have added lots of volume and lift to the hair giving a super bouncy look.

17 Smooth down the top hair and the fringe. Any stray straggly ends? Check with your two mirrors and ask a friend for a close inspection. If there are any wispy bits, damp them and trim away.

18 This cut needs striking eye make-up to play up that thick fringe. To me, the eyes are always the most important part of the look. Mary was made up by expert Sara, freelance make-up artist, with soft, shadowy eyes, plenty of blusher and shiny lips. As you can see, she looks just great.

Karen's hair is thick, but soft. I cut it for her into a long bob which can be blown dry in two ways – styled under or flicked up.

Karen's cut and blow-dry

You need
shampoo, conditioner, towel
comb
clips
scissors
Stylar brush
water spray.

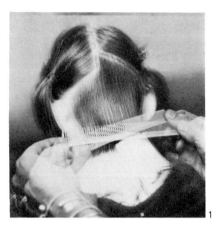

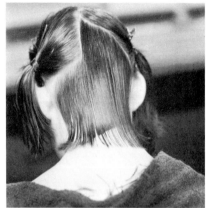

1 Wash, condition and comb through the hair. Now check the growth pattern. Do you want a square or V shape at the nape of the neck? Remember, if short-layered hair is growing out, then a V shape is best. Here you can see both comb angles at once with the help of 'double' photography.

2 Once you've decided, line up your comb and start to cut.

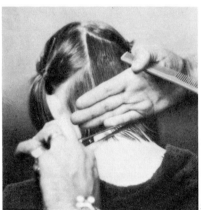

3 Here, I'm using my hand to guide the angle – you may find this easier to do than simply using the comb. Go through the hair slowly and carefully, section by section.

4 Don't pull the hair at ear-level, otherwise there could be a 'hole' as you release it. Use your comb as a guideline for this V angle. Repeat on the other side of the head.

5 Work around the ear, up to the parting. Comb each section down straight.

6 Even up short and long hair where a fringe is growing out.

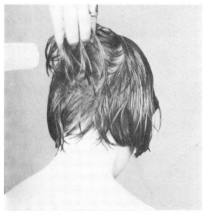

7 It's possible to work from a side or centre parting – as long as you match the sides evenly. Comb through and check the cut. Use a water spray if necessary to re-damp hair and check levels carefully.

8 Towel- or finger-dry hair first, to save time and armache – particularly if you are blowing your own hair dry. You can't put shape into wet hair – in fact, nothing happens at all to the shape of the hair until it's three-quarters dry – only then does the movement start to take place.

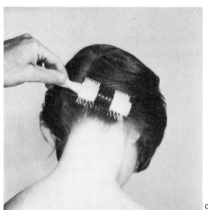

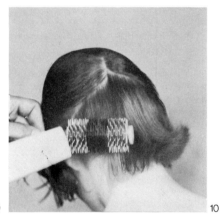

9 First, I blew the style into a soft flip. You must dry the hair roots in an upward movement to give holding power on stubborn hair.

10 Let the Stylar 'grab' the hair almost as if it's a hair roller, to achieve that flip. Hold it in place, and blow with your dryer for a few moments (don't rush – there's no point in releasing the curl too soon, it will simply flop out).

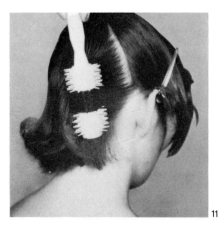

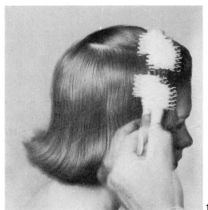

11 Move the Stylar across the hair to get lift from the crown.

12 and 13 At the parting, place the Stylar against the root and lift the hair gently. Not too violently or you'll get a funny 'kink' in the hair.

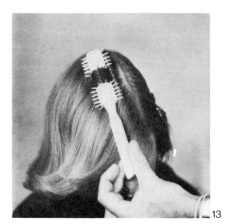

14 Here's where I let Karen finish the job for herself. It looks great.

15 I've now sprayed the hair damp and I'll show you how to use the large Stylar to achieve a soft bob – again, using it as a large roller to turn the hair under. Keep the hand dryer on the move over the full length of the Stylar. That way you won't overdry the hair and create too much electricity. Just follow the shape of the haircut using the Stylar as a soft roller all the way.

16 See the softness and versatility of the style – it really swings and hangs equally well turned under or flipped up. A great style for a beauty-conscious teenager.

12 Hairstyling can be Child's Play

These days, children and teenagers have very firm ideas about what they want from a haircut. Even a five year old can be switched on to fashion and influenced by TV stars, pop singers and magazine pictures.

In the past, haircutting has always been a family problem with children being dragged unwillingly to the barber's, and screeching and wriggling while the poor hairdresser struggled to avoid snipping off an ear-lobe. But now, hair salons are friendly places, used to welcoming the children of their regular clients as well as the 'spec' mothers and children. Most are equipped with high chairs, comics and orange squash to make the children feel at ease. I feel it's a good idea for mothers to familiarize their offspring with haircutting and styling, involving them with shampooing and styling mum's hair as well as their own. If you have a regular appointment with a hairdresser, bring the children along to 'visit' the salon a few times *before* they're brought in for a cut. At home, play a hairdressing game on shampoo night, pretending that the bathroom is a professional salon. Let the children handle, dry and comb through each other's hair.

Who chooses the hair-do? Your child is the one who's got to live with his hairstyle, so that he must like it. I've never pushed my own children into a hairstyle that they hate – I've just explained their hair-type to them and told them how it can be cut and styled to suit their features. Luckily, long, long hair isn't quite as popular now with boys as it was – the school/fashion conflict just doesn't exist. It's possible for a boy to wear a good, fashionable cut and still be within the 'regulation' length limit. A little vanity is a healthy sign in children and they should be encouraged to look at themselves in the mirror and admire their own hair when it's been freshly washed and styled.

What about cutting children's hair at home? This can work well with the easy step-by-step techniques I've described in this book. But do choose your moment! I've often cut my own children's hair when they've been sitting on the potty (a few years ago, naturally), nicely static for a suitable length of time and concentrating on the job in hand. Older children won't want to be dragged away from games or homework for a haircut or 'threatened' with a haircut several hours in advance of the operation. It's better to have scissors ready and sharpened and choose a time when the whole thing will be great fun for everyone and not a hassle for you. Keep scissors out of reach of children.

It's especially important to make a good job of cutting children's hair, as the texture and growth pattern do require careful handling. A bad haircut now can make the hairdresser's job much harder. Many children have fine, fly-away hair which needs careful handling. But, as you will see, a careful logical cut will be fairly simple for most amateurs. For my 'guinea pigs', I chose three children with different types of hair and different requirements.

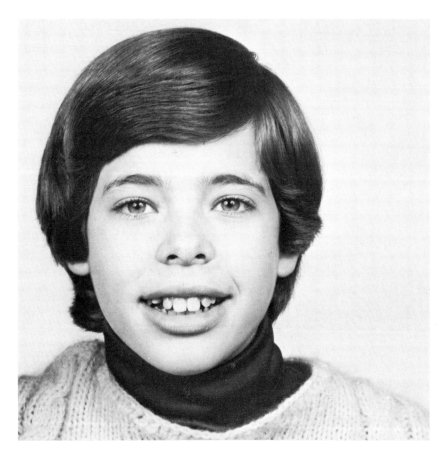

Adam's haircut

Make sure the child is at the right level for his hair-do. Obviously, if he's on the potty, you need to be at floor-level. Otherwise, sit him on a cushion while you stand, or on a low stool between your knees while you sit.

You need
shampoo, conditioner
sharp scissors
comb
towel or cape
suitable chair.

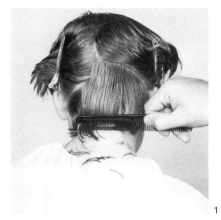

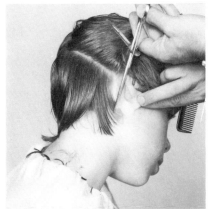

1 Shampoo, condition and comb the hair. Make a centre parting and another, horizontal one, $2\frac{1}{2}''$ from the nape of the neck. Clip side hair out of the way. Now you must decide whether to have a square back or a V-shaped back. If the hair is worn short over the ears, then go for a V-shaped back otherwise it will be too short at the nape. Consider the hair growth pattern. If the child wants a longer look, and is growing out a short, layered cut, then choose a V-shaped nape. However, Adam is having a square-cut back with a trim, vertical line from the back of each ear to join the straight horizontal line at the nape. Line up the first cut with your comb, and trim hair away.

2 Cut down the side hair towards the nape, using your fingertips to gently press the ear-lobe away from the cutting area. Repeat on the other side of the head.

3 Brush down the next layer and repeat the process. Make sure that your lines match up evenly.

4 Start taking vertical sections all around the back of the head, cutting as you go. Don't pull the hair hard as you flatten each ear – you'll cut away too much hair and make a hole.

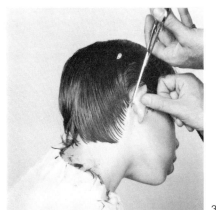

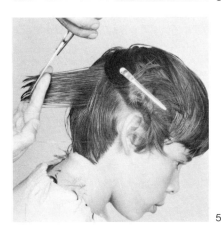

5 Continue with the vertical sections, combing hair downwards and checking the finished line between each one.

6 Use your fingers to hold each section firmly.

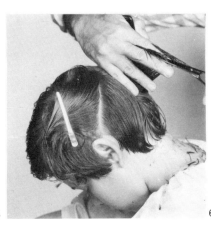

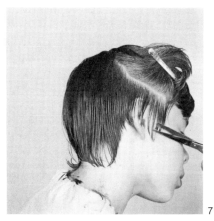

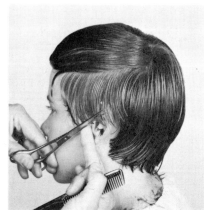

7 Cut the sides in layers making a slightly sloping line from the cheek-bone to the rim of the ear.

8 Comb down the next layer and repeat the process.

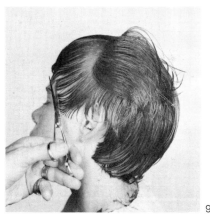

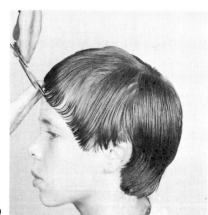

9 Comb fringe area forward – 2″ layer first. Cut into a neat line, using the comb as a guide, and taking into account any shortish layered bits that will grow into the new cut.

10 Comb the full fringe area forward and neaten that line.

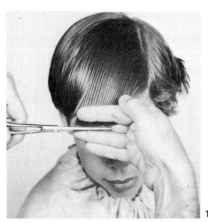

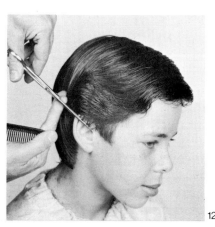

11 Front view of the fringe – not too much cut off, remember.

12 Comb sides back (they should make a super feathered line), and re-check ear-tip stragglers.
Now, blow-dry the style.

Fiona's haircut

Fiona is a 'goldilocks' girl who wants a more grown-up look. Her long hair was difficult to handle and a bit overpowering for her tiny face.

You need
hair brush
shampoo, conditioner
long comb
hair clips

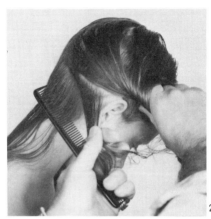

1, 2 and 3 Divide hair into sections, a centre parting and then a horizontal one 2″ from the nape, with the side hair caught up. If clips won't hold long hair securely out of the way, twist a strand of hair around each side section to make bunches.

4 When hair is tied securely back from your working area, line up the length required with your comb. Remember to cut it longer than necessary at first (two reasons: so that you don't make an irreparable mistake, and so that your 'client' isn't too deeply shocked to see a long, long piece of hair on the floor).

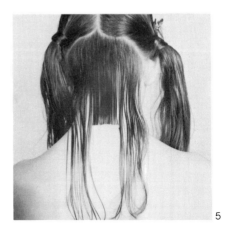

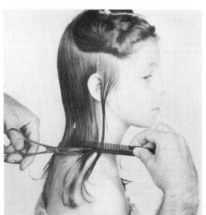

5 and 6 Trim away the central section, then even up all around.

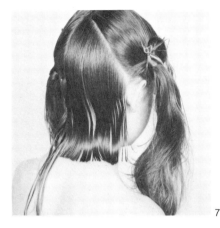

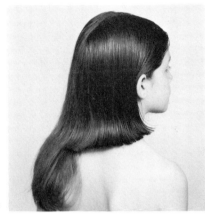

7 Comb down the layers, making a diagonal line across from ear to central parting as you work. Cut each layer into line.

8 One side is super! I cut Fiona's hair like this to show her the difference. Luckily, she loved it.

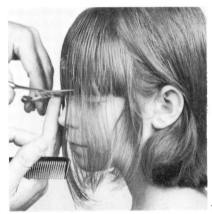

9 Tackle the fringe carefully, starting with the bottom layer of hair. Steady your scissors with your finger, in case your young client sneezes or blinks!

10 Comb down the layers and carry on cutting. Note that Fiona's fringe is at brow level – but this lifts to give a much shorter effect when dried.

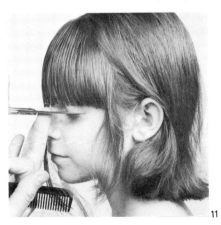

11 Finish the fringe, then go around the whole hairstyle again. You may decide to cut off more. In fact, I did trim a little more off the whole style as I felt it suited Fiona better.

12 Blown dry and swinging for a natural, bouncy look which will keep looking pretty if she dances, plays tennis or jumps for joy. It won't dangle in her eyes as she works at her homework, either.

Justin's haircut

Justin is a cheeky, bright little boy with fine blond 'English' hair that needs washing two or three times a week. It dries quickly, so that I needed a water spray to keep the hair damp while I cut it. The style is similar to Adam's (page 34), but it is cut in wider sections to give more body to the hair as it is cut. Warning – this type of fine hair is very difficult to cut, as every mark shows.

You need
sharp scissors
shampoo, conditioner, towel
comb
water spray.

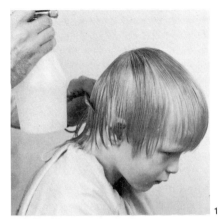
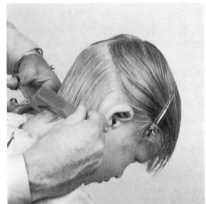

1 Shampoo and condition hair. Comb through. Re-spray with water.

2 Comb down the first layer and use your comb as a cutting guide (a square back, here). Repeat with all the back layers, checking and re-checking cutting line and pulling the hair taught between your fingers.

3 Then start the front hair, side first.

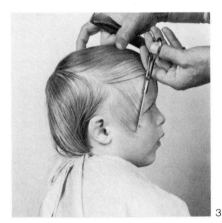
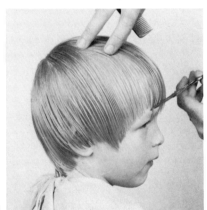

4 Comb down the top front hair, and line up the fringe.

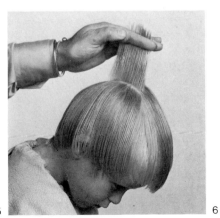

5 The front fringe is cut above eyebrow level.

6 Check those layers.

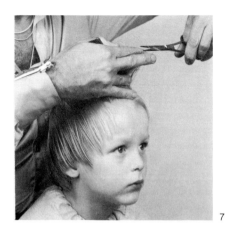

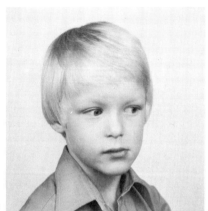

7 Brush through the hair and trim vertically, constantly combing and cutting to give the fine hair a good shape and thicker look.

8 The finished cut – it dried all by itself. A great look for a cheeky chap!

Blow-drying can be fun

Finally, if children learn to care about their hair early, they'll be interested and concerned with hair care all their lives. Make sure they enjoy hairstyling by encouraging a bit of vanity. With two, or more, children in the family you can save yourself a lot of time by teaching them how to play the hairdressing 'game'. Quite young children can be trained to handle a hair dryer properly, to brush their hair into shape and style it themselves, but *supervision* is essential.

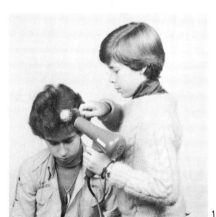

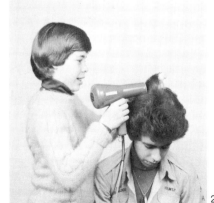

13 Short and Sweet

I love short hair – *if* it's beautifully cut and conditioned. With the right clothes and make-up, short hair can look just as sensuous and attractive as long or medium-length hair. These days, the short cuts are top fashion, too.

But, before you decide to have your hair cut short, do discuss the style with your hairdresser. It will depend to a large extent on the natural growth-pattern, texture and condition of your hair. Plus, of course, your face-shape and way of life. It's a bright idea to look through magazines – or this book – for a possible style to suit your face, figure and pocket. Remember short hair is certainly easier to care for than long, but it *must* be cut regularly (by you or your hairdresser) to look good.

The Cut? It's the same one as in the children's section on pp. 34 and 40.
Thick, coarse hair will usually have enough body to 'hold' a good short cut –
perhaps with tonging or blow-drying to give it shape.
Medium hair may be floppy if it has no natural wave – that's when a light perm
or a tighter, more curly-looking perm is a good idea. If the hair is inclined to be
greasy, the perm will have a useful drying effect.
Very fine hair will certainly need a perm, unless your features are tiny enough
to take a fine, wispy look.

Caring for your Crop Do, by all means, shampoo your short hair-do daily in the
shower. But, unless you have bleached hair, it will be unnecessary to use a
conditioner every day. You will also be fine with just one shampoo. Remember,
the 'mystique' about needing two shampoos really only started in the bad old
days when hairdressing clients washed their hair once a fortnight. They needed
two shampoos – today's daily shower-and-shampoo girl definitely doesn't. In
these pictures you see Alison doing her daily freshen-up routine. She lavishes
as much care on her hair as she does her body, finishing with a cool shower to
leave her hair squeaky-clean and her skin tingling fresh.

To dry short hair Use summer sunshine (why not take your breakfast outside
in the garden after showering and let nature be your own hair dryer?), winter
central heating or, like Alison, use the drying power of an angle-poise lamp
while you're applying your make-up. It really isn't necessary to use the full blast
of a hair dryer on such short hair – when you're washing it often, it's important
to treat it gently. As the hair dries, lift it gently with your fingers to let it
'breathe' and give the shape a little volume.

   After making-up Alison styles her hair with the Leighton Curvar, and her
fingertips.

   For another look she uses setting gel applied lightly to the hair, which is then
combed close to the scalp and smoothed into 'kiss curls', 1950s-style, at the
front and sides. Now this needs more make-up emphasis – red lips, lots of
blusher. It's a fabulous look for a young girl.

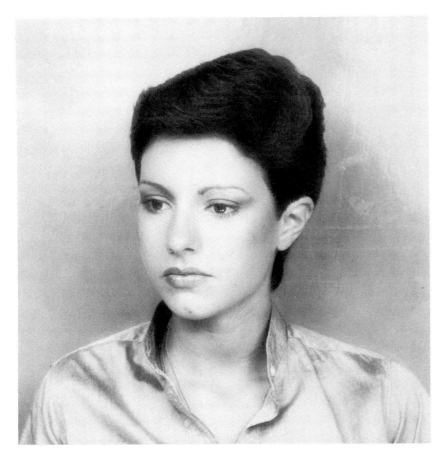

More bounce for your money

Here's the same basic cut as Alison's, worn by Christine. But she feels happier and looks best with slightly more 'bounce' in the shape. So she shampoos in the shower, towel-dries or dries off in the sunshine, then uses curling tongs to give lift.

A tip here: put your comb *under* each section of hair as you tong it, to prevent the hot tongs from touching your scalp. I've seen some painful burns as a result of this. As you look in the mirror, remember that you're 'twirling' your tongs in the opposite direction from the image you see — don't get muddled. Practise with cold tongs before you start, to make sure you do things correctly.

Let your hair cool down, then push your fingers through your hair to give lift and a little more natural bounce. You don't want those tonged curls to look like sausages.

The final hair-do: attractive from all angles.

Mari's new cut

Mari has basically the same cut as worn by Alison, but it varies in that her hair growth is back instead of forward. She styles it simply in two ways – blow-drying and tonging. Here's how you can ring the changes with your short cut:

1 Mari's hair is washed and conditioned then towelled to soak up the excess water. (There's no point in blow-drying soaking wet hair – it takes ages and makes your arm ache.) She brushes the hair forward from the crown, twirling the small Leighton Stylar forward as she goes and lifting the hair from the root.

2 There she blows! Directing the jet of air *forward* to keep that lovely feathery, forward movement. It pays to direct the jet towards the finished movement of the hair for a neat result, otherwise stray wisps could decide to go the other way.

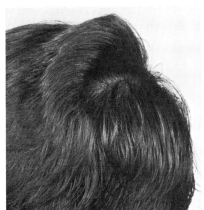

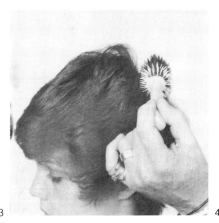

3 Forward from the lower crown, downwards from the same point. You can see the movement in this picture very clearly indeed.

4 Twirling your brush upwards and downwards, dry off the back section.

5 Pay special attention to the fringe area, lifting the hair gently.

6 That 'twirling' action in close-up. Never pull the hair; you should always condition and comb it through before you start to style the hair – no knots, please!

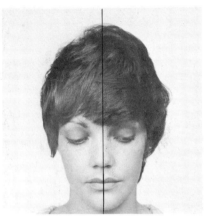

7 The side hair is blown and brushed forwards.

8 The finished look. See how different one side looks if it's allowed to dry naturally – it just hasn't got the same lift and fashionable look. I feel that only the shortest short cuts or permed hair-dos should be allowed to dry naturally without that little extra polish that comes from blow-drying.

Mari's tonged look

For slightly more movement and lift, this is an easy cut to tong into shape. Here's how:

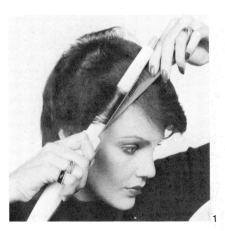

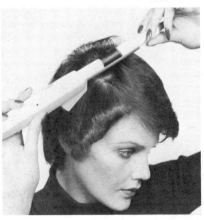

1 Start with the side hair. Comb underneath the tongs to prevent burning. Twirl under, hold, then release tongs.

2 Work over the crown next, keeping that comb in position for each 'twirl'.

3 Back to the front hair – the neat little 'sausages' are building up nicely.

4 Final twirl at the side of the hair. Release tongs and switch off. Don't burn your bed or dressing-table top!

5 Allow curls to cool down – if you're in a hurry and it isn't raining, you can always pop your head out of the window.

6 Now brush hair *against* the direction you want it to fall – to give more volume. Style forward with brush and fingertips.

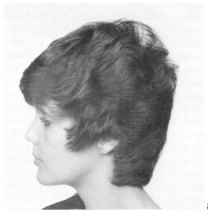

7 and 8 Always check your hair-do from the side and back, using a small hand mirror and your larger mirror. I see a lot of girls with super hair at the front, but with ends sticking up at the back. Half the world sees your *back* view.

Short and curly

Two very different looks from the same basic cut. One is permed and blown dry, the other left natural and tonged into shape.

Lots of girls and men are hooked on the short, curly perm. It's easy to see why: it's simple to look after, pretty and very sexy. Somehow, those curls just cry out to be ruffled.

If you have a short, permed hair-do like Sue (her basic cut is the same as the graduated one we used for Mari's perm on page 47 – just shorter), do look after it. It needs normal conditioning often and handling with care. Don't be tempted to have it re-permed until the existing perm can be cut off completely – otherwise you'll get a dry, woolly mop with nasty split ends. Here's how Sue cares for her curly hair-do:

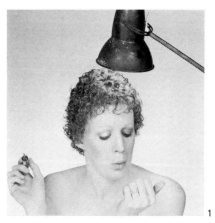

1 After washing and conditioning in the shower, she lets it dry under an angle-poise lamp while she does her manicure. This gives a natural, curly look for every day – looks great with eye make-up and casual clothes.

2 If she wants a softer look, Sue blows her damp hair dry and styles it with my Stylar, keeping the nozzle of the hair dryer a few inches away from her hair and twirling the Stylar in upward movements, lifting the hair from the crown.

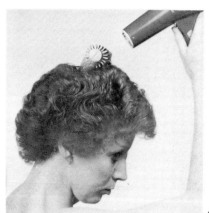

3 and 4 An extra lift for that crown section just to soften the curl.

5 No combing – just a quick lift with the fingertips.

6 The finished hair-do.

14 How to Cope with Long Hair

If you love long hair — and it suits you — then wear it long. Don't be brow-beaten by your hairdresser into having it cut off just to satisfy his styling urges if you're sure that long hair is 'you'.

But you must be prepared to spend time and effort on making your hair look good if you wear it long. Logically, it's going to take extra time to wash, dry and style your hair — if this fits into your lifestyle, fine. You must avoid allowing your hair to become dirty, greasy or split-ended. So shampoo regularly, use a conditioner and have those ends cut off frequently (or do it yourself, if you like). To save yourself too much armache, try allowing your hair to dry naturally if it's straight or has a natural wave. At least, allow it to dry off quite a bit before blow-styling it, otherwise you'll lose patience in no time and put off shampooing until your hair is really dirty.

Most models with long hair shampoo it in the bath or shower, then wrap it in a towel while they eat breakfast. This successfully absorbs most of the excess water. Afterwards, they dry off the hair and then tong or Carmen it. I know one model girl who washes her hair on summer mornings, and then goes for a ride on her pony. She comes back with shiny, dry hair 'blown' into long, sleek shape by the force of the wind. Not recommended for chilly days, though.

Keep a close watch on those ends — most people have a natural 'limit' on a successful hair-length. After, say, ten inches of growth, the hair often starts to split and just doesn't want to be worn longer. Listen to what it's trying to tell you. No amount of care will mend split ends — they must be cut off.

Experiment with your hair so that you can ring the changes with styling. Chignons, worn at the nape of the neck, are fashionable and stylish but look best on the very young (older women look too severe with chignons, generally). Slides and combs look nice on neat, shiny hair too. Don't be a slave to your heated rollers — used daily, they'll break your hair in time. Always wrap each roller in a tissue before winding up long hair to prevent tangling and breakage.

Those hundred strokes a day? No! Limit brushing to a few gentle strokes to remove dirt and to give shine. Too much brushing will only encourage greasiness and could damage the hair. If you have your long hair tinted, streaked or bleached, treat it very gently indeed. For the ends of the hair are already several years old, and may be feeling just a little worn out.

Two of my friends with long hair are Jane and Sharon, a mother and daughter who share the same lovely eyes and beautiful features.

Sharon is sixteen and longs to be a model. She should succeed, for she was a 'natural' for our pictures. Her hair is very long and fairly easy to handle, but she's growing out a fringe which has been rather a problem. I advised her to *use* that short, awkward bit of hair instead of letting it flop about looking untidy. Here's how we styled her long hair:

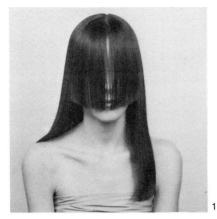

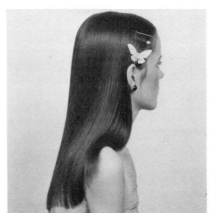

1 That problem fringe. If you're growing one out, like Sharon, you must still trim it regularly otherwise the ends will split and 'show' more amongst your smooth long hair. When you shampoo it, comb the fringe forward and cut it straight across, snipping away just one-eighth of an inch, or more, if you have to line up odd lengths.

2 Let your hair dry naturally or help it with a dryer. You can tame that fringe with setting gel. Just take it out of the jar with your fingertips, smooth it on the front of your hair, comb through and catch in place with a single slide or a combination of pretty grips and a butterfly slide.

3 Smooth on more gel for this style, covering that awkward fringe. Twist the hair towards the back, and secure in place with a slide.

4 The gel helps hold a chignon in place too. Just twist and knot the hair at the nape as if you were knotting a piece of string. Secure with grips and a slide.

Note: if you've never used gel before, here's how to remove it. Shampoo straight onto gel area, work up a lather and rinse. Or, rinse out the gel before you shampoo.

Jane is a freelance caterer and often helps out in a restaurant. When cooking, it's best to fasten long hair back in a pony tail (very fashionable again) to keep it away from fumes and grease. This also helps to shape her hair into a pageboy look for her evening style.

Jane has a similar hair growth pattern to Sharon's. The hair falls from her brow and is naturally thick and smooth, the perfect type of hair for a long look.

Use tissue (loo paper will do) around rollers before doing that evening hair-do. For quickness, Jane does her make-up while her rollers 'take'. Use a styling spray if you like. Unwind rollers carefully (don't rush — you'll tear your hair), and allow to cool.

Brush through for a soft, sexy style. Don't back-comb the crown. Many women with long hair have permanent tangles on top through excessive back-combing. It shows and looks ugly.

15 Supercurl!

If you've got naturally curly hair, don't moan. Just relax and enjoy it! I'm right against straightening curly hair, simply because the straightening products on the market at the moment are just too harsh for safe use. But even if they were perfectly safe, I'd still be disinclined to advise a client with curls to have them straightened. For curls, cut the right way, can look sensational.

Mary Anne is a beautiful actress and model, with naturally curly short hair. She must be able to wash and handle her hair easily as she must always be available for a possible audition and can't spend her time having too many professional treatments. Like many black girls, Mary Anne has very dry hair. So, I showed her how to give her hair a professional softening, conditioning treatment herself. Here's how:

Use a good conditioner — we chose Clairol's conditioner — and massage it well first into the scalp and then the ends of the hair. Now wrap your hair in self-sticking food-wrap film and leave the conditioner on for one or two hours. If you don't have that much time, hand-dry the film with a jet of warm air for twenty to thirty minutes or take a warm bath — anything to warm that conditioner thoroughly. Do this once a week if your hair is very dry. Now rinse thoroughly, towel dry and leave to dry naturally or tong lightly for a more formal look.

Mary Anne looks great with a pretty flower tucked behind one ear for an evening date.

Mid-length and wavy

It's best to keep naturally curly hair one length and keep it thick at the ends, not graduated. Why? Because thin curly hair will tend to swell and frizz at the ends when it's washed.

Kitty has lovely, naturally wavy hair which looks very glamorous worn medium-long. Have *you* got this type of hair? Here's how you, or your hairdresser, should cut it:

1 Comb hair through and judge just how much hair needs to come off to thicken up the ends satisfactorily. Start by combing hair straight down to the shoulders. Use your comb as a guideline as you start to cut. Make a centre parting, then another horizontal parting about $2\frac{1}{2}''$ from the nape of your neck. Tie or clip back side hair firmly.

2 Using your comb as a guideline, start to cut the hair in small sections – not too much at a time – until the whole section is cut into line.

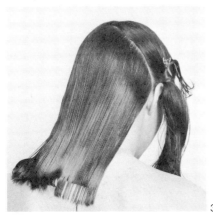

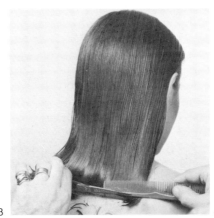

3 Now bring down the next section, taken from a parting $2\frac{1}{2}''$ above the first one. Cut into line, again using your comb as a guide. It's rather like matching bricks – one section on top of the other. But you must keep the cut even and square.

4 Difficulty with that comb? You can use your hand as a guideline if you like, but check and re-check that your line is a straight one. Follow the shape around from shoulder-level to ear-level, keeping it straight. Don't pull hair too hard or the springiness of the natural curl could cause a fuzzy line and a graduated effect which you must avoid.

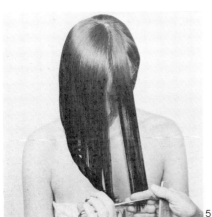

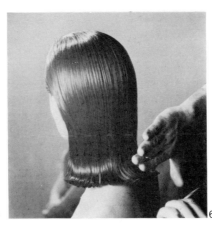

5 Comb hair forward from the crown down over the eyes and keep that square shape firmly in mind. Use the shoulders as a horizontal guideline to judge your cutting line, which should always be parallel to the natural shoulder line. Beware of slouchers – the hair will be cut off balance.

6 Now check shape and comb hair back and into position – double-checking the cut all around the length.

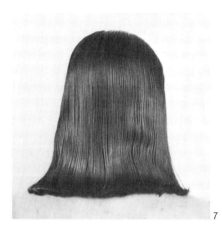

7 Allow the hair to dry naturally, and just brush with my Curvar into an attractive shape.

8 A style that's dateless, sexy, smashing! Yours with naturally wavy hair and a square, symmetrical cut.

Long and frizzy

Paula has very, very curly hair — and she likes to wear it long and straight. The two just don't mix and Paula is now paying the price for two or three straightening treatments in the past year. Her hair has broken off at the front and it is weak and spongy. Any hard brushing will automatically cause the hair to snap.

I advise her to forget straightening treatments and to concentrate on conditioning her own hair with monthly at-home treatments like the one I prescribed for Mary Anne. As for that long, sleek look, I advise her to set her hair on huge rollers, section by section, and to brush through when dry with a solid cream brilliantine or just a little water to give shine and control. Brushing and using a blow-dryer at the same time will relax the curl and straighten it out

Long and frizzy

slightly. Another tip for Paula: wash and condition hair, then tie it at the nape or on top of the head and make-up or potter around the house. On releasing the covered elastic band the hair will lie much flatter. You can use the same trick if your hair is wild, curly and long enough to secure with a band.

But Paula can have the look of long, glamorous, straightish hair and probably much more successfully than many girls with dead straight locks. Although frizzy, her hair is easy to handle and hold in place. To achieve her super upswept chignon, follow her, step-by-step:

1 Wash, condition and towel-dry hair. Then set in small sections on large rollers. Fringe back from the face, back hair going under.

2 Check to see if hair is thoroughly dry (if not, that frizz will reappear).

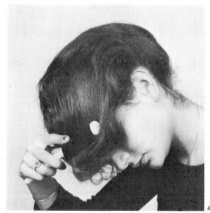

3 and 4 Take out rollers, and dab on a solid cream brilliantine. Now brush foward using a blow-dryer to relax and curl and straighten your hair still more.

5 Brush back, still using that blow-dryer.

6 Lift front hair with your fingers. This is Paula's broken fringe area – but she's able to use it as a pretty part of the style.

7 Smooth side and back hair and lift front right-hand section.

8 Pin onto the crown with hair-pins and/or grips.

9 Using the first grips or pins as an anchor, brush hair upwards all the way around, and secure on top.

10 Leave that fringe area naturally curly and soft.

11 Allow a curl or two to escape at the nape of the neck, and tidy the top section by swirling all the loose ends into a knot.

12 The finished look – romantic, smooth and luxuriant. Definitely much more so because Paula has frizzy hair with lots of body but knows just how to control it.

16 How to be a Permanent Success

Perming is tricky, for the professional hairdresser and for the amateur. I'm constantly hearing tales of disasters and clearing up the damage caused by bad perming – dry hair, breaking hair, strange colours. Timing is a vital part of the process. Unless your stylist is experienced with expert knowledge of the products he's using (and they're powerful products, make no mistake), he could make an error. A good hairdresser will examine the condition of your hair first, before even thinking about a perm. If it's streaked or highlighted, if the ends are split or if the hair is thin or over-bleached, he'll probably advise against it. If you have permed ends, your hairdresser should advise a cut to remove these – perm upon perm means split ends and dryness. A course of conditioning treatments may be advised before the 'perm' day. You can tell if your hairdresser has plenty of perming experience, if he makes all these observations and is frank about what can and cannot be achieved with your hair.

What happens to hair when it's permed? The perming chemicals actually penetrate the hair shaft to the cuticle and rearrange the molecules that make up the protein-based hair. Instead of a straight-line pattern, the molecules make a curvy, wavy line. They are then 'set' in this new pattern by the neutralizing process. The rearranged molecules may 'relax' slightly with some perms a few days after you have the perm. Remember, perming is permanent and is there until it grows out. Nowadays, there are safe, gentle perms for most kinds of hair (apart from the conditions mentioned above) including tinted and lightened hair. And most have built-in conditioners and buffers to prevent over-perming. But, they are still tricky things to apply well.

Before perming at home check the manufacturer's instructions on the pack. This applies to home perm users or professionals using professional products. If you don't understand the instructions, don't use the product. Many manufacturers do have advisers whom you can write to for more information and, naturally, all hold seminars for young and mature hairdressers.

Study the result you want before starting the perm. If you're going to your hairdresser, find a magazine picture that looks like the kind of result you have in mind. He'll be able to tell you if it's a possibility or not with your type of hair. If a friend is doing the job for you, shop around first and study the various perms on the market before choosing the right one.

Does your hair need cutting? If you're having a professional perm, the hairdresser will naturally advise you on this. But if you're having a home perm, you may need a professional cut first. Many home perms turn out badly and look home-permed, simply because the hair hasn't been properly cut as a first step. The result is badly shaped, tatty-looking and 'endy'.

Perming – step-by-step

Mari is a tall, elegant lady with medium-length dark brown hair. She's a model, so must look marvellous at all times. As you can see from the smaller picture, her lank, straightish hairstyle does not complement her really beautiful features. She has a long face which needs hair volume and softness to complement it.

I decided to keep the basic length of the hair (perming makes hair look shorter, remember), but to put more graduation through the crown length to achieve that soft volume. Is your hair rather like Mari's? Here's how we – and you or your hairdresser – can make it a permanent success.

You need
perm kit, including rollers, papers
shampoo, conditioner
scissors
clips
comb
plastic food-wrapping film
long wooden orange sticks.

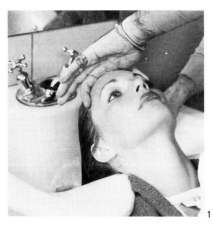

1 First the hair must be shampooed carefully. Damp the hair with tepid to warm water.

2 Pour the shampoo into your hand, not directly onto the hair – that way, you prevent it from vanishing down the sink.

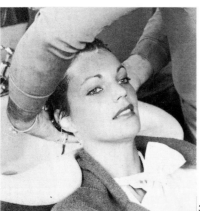

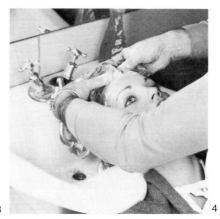

3 Apply shampoo to the ends of the hair and develop the lather.

4 Massage well into the hairline at the front of the hair, first with your thumbs, then with the pads of your fingertips applying gentle pressure. Work your way all around the hairline. This is important as these are the greasy, make-up-clogged areas – if your perm is to 'take' satisfactorily, all this grease must be removed. Work in circular movements towards the centre of the crown, repeating again and again. Then re-wash ends of hair.

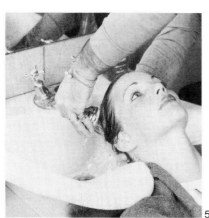

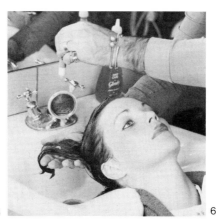

5 Rinse hair very thoroughly and repeat the process. If the hair is normally washed daily or two or three times a week, it's only necessary to give one wash.

6 Now apply conditioner – but keep it from the scalp as this causes grease build-up which will interfere with the perm. Comb through and rinse thoroughly.

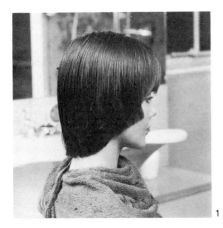

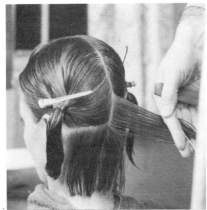

Now for the pre-perm cut

1 This shows the finished cut. Although it looks like a neat Florentine bob, the cut is actually in many layers – around 4″ on the crown, 2″ at the nape of the neck.

2 Make a centre parting from forehead to nape of neck, then another, vertical parting 2″ above the nape. Comb bottom hair down, and secure side hair away with large clips. Now lift hair in vertical sections between two fingers and slope your scissors towards the head as you cut. This makes the top part of each section slightly shorter than the underneath part.

3, 4, 5 and 6 Continue this process all over the back hair, making the lower section long, and graduating the rest. I call this method of cutting 'feel and touch', because I let each section of cut and uncut hair fall into my fingers so that I can gauge the effect. I then repeat the process working left to right across the sides of the hair.

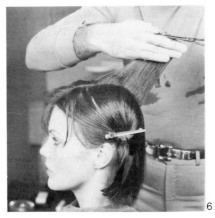

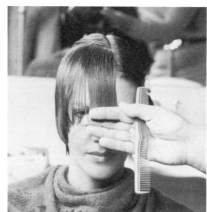

7 Now work on the sides. Comb forward onto the cheeks to give softness, and check your line for straightness with your comb. Repeat with the other side of the hair, keeping the top and fringe hair securely fastened up out of the way.

8 Comb fringe hair down towards the nose – a 2″ central section to begin with. Now measure and judge the fringe level – remembering, again, that perming gives a shorter look to the finished hairstyle.

9 Don't cut the fringe hair straight across. Instead, cut it in vertical sections, lifting each one and cutting the top bit of each section slightly shorter than the underneath hair to give a feathery effect. Otherwise, the perm will give a too-heavy look to that front hair – we want lightness, and volume, not a 'dragged-down' look.

10 Repeat the process, working from left to right (or right to left, if you're left-handed) across the front of the hair.

11 Comb hair through, combing fringe area and sides forward and use your comb as a guide for the straightness of each line. It's important for the finished cut to be neat.

12 The final cut – all edges clean as a whistle. Damp hair down with a water spray here if you need to check pristine neatness. As you can see, the hair looks all one length – but it is softly graduated all over.

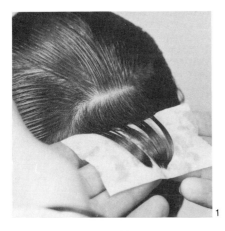

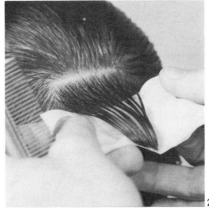

How to wind a perm curler

Make sure you read the instructions on the box and accompanying leaflet before you start your perm. Here's a step-by-step account of just how to wind up a curler. In my experience, incorrect *winding* is responsible for most perm disappointment – kinky ends, insufficient 'lift' to the hair section, often they can both be traced back to bad winding.

1 When you've combed and divided the wet hair into the correct sections, take a perm paper and hold it under the section to be curled.

2 Now fold the sides of the paper inwards.

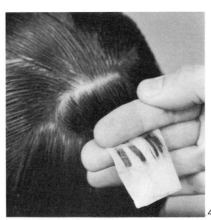

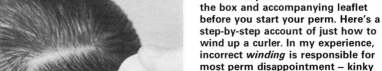

3 Damp the paper using a water spray or lotion depending on the product and smooth down paper between first two fingers to make it neat.

4 Grip section firmly between first two fingers near the root of the hair.

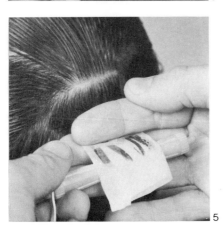

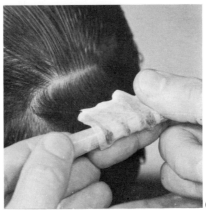

5 Place correct-size curler underneath the paper and tuck paper under cleanly – no kinks or wrinkles.

6 and 7 Wind under, lifting the roller as you go – the more you lift the more volume you'll get with your finished perm.

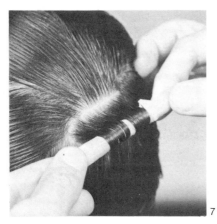

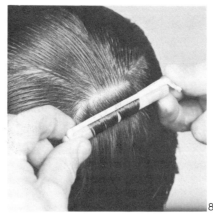

8 Bring elastic over to fasten, checking that it isn't catching in any loose hair. If you have wound in any loose bits, you must undo the curler and start again. As the wind-up is completed, damp thoroughly with perm lotion. If hair is longer than about 3″ all over you must damp the hair with perm lotion before winding up. (But do refer to the particular instructions of the manufacturer.)
It pays dividends to practise this winding procedure before attempting the actual perm, and even to practise on somebody else before you use the perm lotion.

Mari's wind-up

1 Divide hair into five sections: one long section from the front of the hair, right across the crown to the nape of the neck, and two smaller sections each side. My curler-count for the five sections: twenty-three along the long section, twelve for each back side section and five for each front side section (see picture five). Start with the long, central section, clipping the side hair securely away from the hair you're working with.

2 Starting from the crown, position and wind up rollers (using the method described above), working downwards towards the nape of the neck, and damping with perm lotion as you go.

3 As soon as you have completed six rollers, slip a wooden cuticle stick underneath the elastic. This stops the bands from cutting into the hair, particularly on the vulnerable crown, forehead and temples. You could get a series of little kinks in your curls if you leave the elastic bands touching the hair, and the hair could snap off.

4 and 5 Work right down to nape, then switch to the front of the main section, working forward towards the nose (five or six rollers). Complete sides, working downwards towards neck.

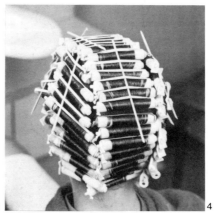

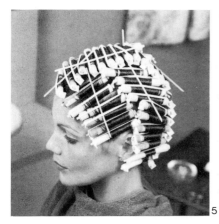 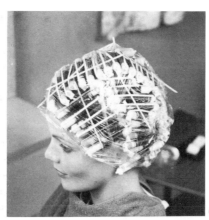

6 When the perm rollers are in position and damped with lotion, place some cling film food wrap all around the head while the perm develops.

 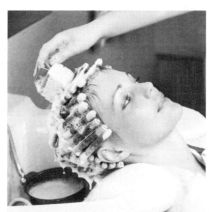

7 Study those instructions again for neutralizing the perm. Here you can see that she has rinsed it really thoroughly first.

8 and 9 On this perm, the neutralizer is applied with a sponge, allowed to develop and then the rollers are removed. But do follow your own perm instructions carefully. Sorry to keep saying this, but so many people just don't.

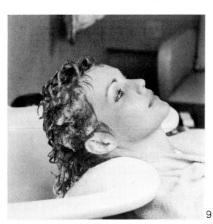 

10 With her hair rinsed and just placed in position with my fingers, Mari looks marvellous. As you can see, the curl is even and the shape good.

How to brush and style the perm I styled Mari's permed hair in two ways. First, we just left it to dry naturally, lifting the hair gently for volume and placing it with our fingers. Then, for a different look, I softly blow-styled the hair using my No. 1 Stylar – this gives it a chic look for a party, with plenty of sex appeal.

Brush gently forward from the crown, flicking the fringe back and to one side as you dry. Repeat this process all around the hair, flicking up the ends gently.

It's the cut that counts The secret of the success of Mari's perm was undoubtedly that super base cut on page 69. That's why her finished style has such volume and lift. The same cut is also ideal for longer hair with natural body and curl. Here, you see Shelley who has exactly the same graduated cut as Mari, but I set her hair on rollers (no perm), then softly blowed it dry and brushed it through. As the cut is graduated, her hair has natural lift and movement despite the *length*. So, perm or not, it's really the cut that counts!

17 Hairstyles for the Hectic Life

'Keep it simple' is my rule for career girl hair-dos. A beautiful cut, excellent condition and pretty colour will keep you looking good however pressured life becomes.

You should also choose an *adaptable* style which you can pretty-up with slides and/or rollers. You must be able to handle your hair yourself if you can't visit the hairdresser regularly – you don't want to be caught out with tacky, unwashed hair when you have an important date or social engagement.

If you have a busy life, talk to your hairdresser about it and ask him to show you how to blow-dry your hair into swinging shape. I've 'trained' dozens of high-powered, glamorous ladies to care for their hair themselves – here are some of the tips I've passed on:

Heated Rollers If you're busy, you probably rely on heated rollers for 'instant' glamour. As you know, the regular daily use of rollers can be drying and cause split ends. Try to limit roller-use to every other day. Wind tissue around each roller to avoid tangling your hair and to stop those frantic unwinding sessions that usually end up with lots of your hair left tangled around the roller. Check that the ends of your hair are flat against the roller before you wind up – if there's a kink or bend at the end, you'll speed up the splitting process. I recommend the Carmen 'Cascade' Conditioning roller set with a built-in conditioning lotion to care for your hair. If you are away on holiday your hair may suffer from dryness with the sunshine and salt water. If you do not have a Cascade set, simply apply conditioning setting lotion before winding up.

After removing rollers, always allow your hair to cool down thoroughly before brushing into shape. Otherwise, the set won't last.

Colour Choose a colour that's near your natural one so that re-growth won't be too much of a problem. Or, have fine streaks expertly applied regularly – then, if you miss an appointment, the hair will still look good. Book your colour appointment on a day when life is slightly less hectic than usual – don't ask the girl to 'slap it on quickly, please'; she may do just that, and cause unnecessary overlap and a bad result. If you travel abroad, have your colour applied by your regular hairdresser before your trip or visit a recommended salon (it pays to check in advance, if you can). You can't expect exactly the same result from a hairdresser in a different part of the world, but your own 'crimper' will gladly give you a copy of the formula he uses for your hair colour and the product names before you go. Then, if you can find a stylist with the same products (so many are internationally available these days), you stand more chance of a good colour result.

If you have to 'grow out' a colour – light blonde, for instance – you can still look smart. Simply select a toning colour for the ends (choose a shade lighter than your normal colour) and ask your hairdresser to put 'reverse' highlights in it to streak in the re-growth colour. But your hair will need more general care during this time with regular cutting and conditioning. You definitely do need a good stylist to help you through this period.

Shape You need a simple cut to look 'expensive' and well-groomed. One of the cuts in this book will be suitable (the fringed bob on page 25, the mid-long cut on page 29, for instance). If you have a fringe, learn to trim it yourself so that it never looks straggly. If your hair is longer, experiment with clips and slides for an elegant evening look. Hair-pieces? Not unless you're brilliant at putting them on. Frankly, shining real hair is much more attractive.

Equipment Every busy woman should have a good set of heated rollers (preferably the 'Cascade' type), several combs and, of course, my styling brushes. She should also know her hair type and shampoo requirements – perhaps buying her own stock from her hairdresser. Tongs are also very useful for quick refresher techniques and for the smart 'flick-back' fringes. Hair dryer choice? Light, but a good blow-dryer. If you travel a lot, make sure you have adaptor plugs. There's nothing more upsetting than to arrive at a foreign hotel just in time for a romantic dinner to find that your heated rollers won't work. Grips, hair-pins and conventional rollers are also useful. Remember, if you're stuck with fused rollers in a foreign country you can always make soft, bouncy rollers from cotton wool and secure them with hair-pins. Watch for harder or softer water than you're used to if you wash your hair away from home. Use plenty of conditioner to calm down fly-away hair. If your hotel is overheated (and many of them are), watch out for greasy hair. You may find that you must wash your hair or have it washed locally even though your hair normally stays clean and swinging for up to a week. If in doubt, take your dryer, shampoo and rollers with you.

Condition Pressure can cause alarming changes in hair condition. If you're living at a fast pace, supplement your diet with Vitamin B and iron to 'feed' your hair and help it cope. Try to relax between jobs and get some exercise, however hectic your lifestyle. Dandruff and over-greasiness or sudden lankness can be your body's message to you that you're overdoing things – take heed! Unfortunately the kind of people who live a fast life are also those who often want to ring the changes with hair colour and style. If you want perm after perm and a new colour every few weeks, and also work and play hard, your hair will rebel. Be bright and take a lesson from the chic women who're always rushing around – Jackie O., Helen Gurley Brown, Deidre McSharry, Charlotte Rampling, Lauren Bacall. They all tend to stick to one basic shape and colour, with subtle changes each season. They're more likely to be seen having a conditioning treatment than a radical colour change. If you're not familiar with the excellent new salon conditioning treatments available, see my product section at the end of the book. Today, most problems can be solved with correct salon treatment or a consultation with a trichologist.

Remember, in this situation your hair enemies are overwork, jet-lag, temperature changes, harsh treatment, slavish fashion following. Slow down, eat protein, and treat it gently!

Now meet the two most important career women in my life. Caroline Neville, Glemby International Press and Public Relations person, and Maxine Leighton, my wife. Both are bright, beautiful, dynamic ladies with a well-developed hair care sense. I've looked after their hair for many years and admire the way they cope with it even when I'm away on my travels.

Caroline Neville is a thirty-four-year-old mother who also runs an internationally successful public relations consultancy. She has two small children and a busy businessman husband. She runs her business from Greenwich, London, and travels to the Continent and New York regularly.

Her hair is very important to her — she has to look good all the time, whether she's in Paris for a business conference or attending speech day at her son's school. Like most working women she feels much more confident if her hair is looking good — which is why she pays a great deal of attention to her beauty programme. If all this sounds as if she's got plenty of time to beautify herself, don't be fooled. Life is so hectic that only careful organization and forward planning can ensure trouble-free hair care. Caroline literally never knows when she'll be jetting off to Paris or Rome, so that she has to be continually prepared.

Her routine? Caroline's style is medium length and she has it cut by me every six weeks. Her fair highlights are expertly done at a salon every six to eight weeks. Caroline finds that they add volume and body to her hair as well as look pretty.

She washes her hair every three to four days. Every three weeks she applies a wax treatment (Henna) in the bath, relaxes for half an hour and then shampoos. This gives a glossy look and helps beat any condition problems through change of temperature, environment, pace and diet.

Caroline sets her hair on Carmen rollers — the Cascade set with its own

setting/conditioning lotion. She travels with a small set of heated rollers and six ordinary rollers in case her adaptor plugs don't fit. She relies, too, on my 'brushes' for handling and styling her hair.

She loves wearing tortoise-shell slides to clip her hair back in an elegant daytime look, or diamante ones for the evening.

Maxine Leighton, my wife, is another busy lady. She's an active, vibrant person who designs and makes clothes for herself and friends. She often helps serve in a boutique, gives the best dinner parties in town and is a marvellous mother to our two boys. She loves to look elegant in beautiful clothes and is equally at home in jeans. She has the ability to change her look according to what she's doing — which might be chatting to a builder about her latest interior decorating scheme or preparing a delicious meal for the family or friends.

Her hair is very important to her — and to me. After all, a hairdresser is often judged by his wife's hair. At the time we photographed Maxine she was growing out her fringe in order to change her 'look' into one with more movement and curl. Although I was helping her through this transition stage, she had to cope with most of it herself as I travel for about six months of every year. She blow-styled her fringe into an upwards movement so that it looked

pretty during the growing-out stage.

For many years, Maxine was a blonde, but she decided to grow her bleach out recently. I came home one day and found that, with a re-growth of about one inch, she'd taken matters into her own hands and toned down her hair with Clairol's Lotion Toner from their Born Blonde series. She had wisely picked a fairly light shade from the range – with porous, bleached ends a darker shade would not have 'taken' well and could easily have looked artificial and hard.

Later, I naturalized her hair – that's highlights put in with a tint to keep a streaky look while the bleach is growing out. I'm the most critical guy around when it comes to hair colour, but her hair really looked very good indeed throughout the whole growing-out period. Now, she's settled for a tawny-brown colour which is delicious with her new, softly curling look.

18 Two's Company

Lots of girls cut their fellas' hair – especially when the cut is going just a bit straggly between visits to the hairdresser. I'm all for it – as long as the cutting is done the correct way, and doesn't make the hairdresser's job that much more difficult next time.

Ian and Sue started off with a shower and shampoo, gently massaging each other's hair and scalp. After the shower, Sue let her curly permed hair dry naturally (read more about her style on page 52), then set to work to cut and style Ian's straggly locks. Try the same technique on *your* man:

Before you cut Shampoo, condition and comb through your man's hair. Make sure you *do* use conditioner, even if he doesn't usually bother. For the hair will be much easier to cut tangle-free and look really shiny afterwards. He may even be converted into using a conditioner regularly.

You need
shampoo, conditioner
Scotch tape
sharp cutting scissors
clips to hold wet hair
blow-styling and brushing brushes
comb
blow-dryer
mirror for him (as long as he doesn't put you off by moving his head and criticizing. If in doubt, pretend you can't find one until it's all over.).

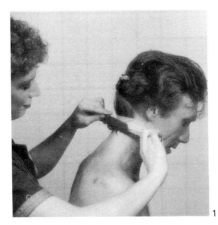 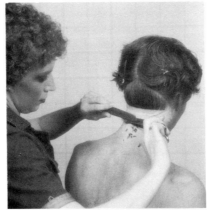

1 Make a parting 2″ above the nape of the neck, horizontally across the nape of the neck. Clip the hair above this line securely up and away from your bottom 2″ section. You'll probably need two clips. Now tape this section of hair securely, using two strips of tape if necessary. Leave the uneven ends of the hair exposed below tape-level.

2 Now, using the straight side of your comb as a cutting guide, trim away the straggly ends with sharp scissors.

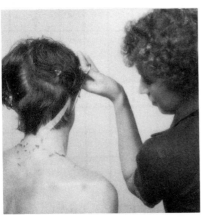 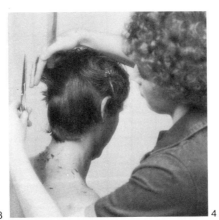

3 Remove the first strip of tape, and comb through the hair. Now place another strip of Scotch tape in a diagonal line from the top of his ear to a point at the middle of the nape of his neck. Trim away the exposed hair to make a neat V shape. Remove the tape, and repeat at the other side – making sure that the two sides match perfectly.

4 Work vertically around the back of the head, taking the hair firmly between the first two fingers of your left hand, and cutting away the straggly ends with your free hand. Bring hair down from the clipped-back sections as you need to. You must cut a little at a time on a short hair-do such as this one.

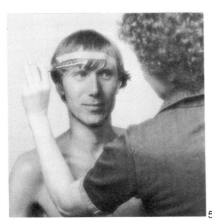 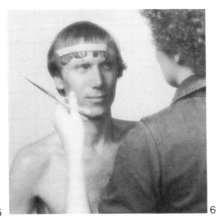

5 Start work on that all important front section of his hair. Comb the hair forward (making the parting in the position he usually wears it). Tape across the fringe to secure the hair as you work. Now cut, in short sections, across the fringe, clearing his brows, but without cutting too much hair away.

6 Take a breather, step back, and assess the fringe. Is it straight? Is it short enough (bearing in mind that dry hair tends to 'shrink' a little)? Let him check in the mirror if you like.

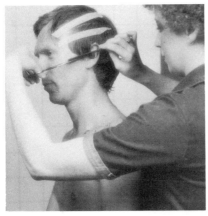

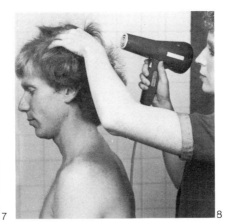

7 Now work on the left side of his head. Comb the hair down from the parting, and tape up securely as shown (two rows of tape). Using your comb as a guide, cut a straight line at mid-ear level – sloping slightly forwards. If you line up your comb with his nose and ear, you'll pick the most flattering place for the cut. Repeat the process, the other side of his head, to complete the cut.

8 Blow-dry his hair carefully (most men love this bit), using your fingers to style and control the hair.

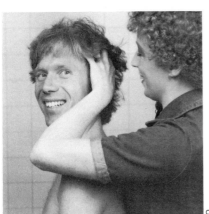

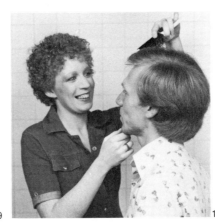

9 Lift the side hair, and smooth it back with your fingers if his hair is short and fine. If it's longer and thicker use one of my brushes to blow-style it into shape and control it while you dry.

10 Now make the parting neatly and comb the style into shape. Neat, well-groomed, masculine – a really great cut by a great girl!

19 Loving Style

Would *you* dare to cut your girlfriend's hair? If *she* has a simple style which just needs regular cutting to stay in good shape, then there's no reason why *he* can't be trained to cut her hair between visits to the professional stylist.

Mac is a busy model who's always changing her look to suit the jobs she has to do. She rushes around and doesn't have too much time to spend at the hairdresser's. So, she relies on a professional perm to make her hair easier to control. It's very fine indeed, and without the perm it would be lank and go greasy quickly. She's trying to grow it longer, keeping the basic shape. She must keep the nape hair blunt to give body and easy handling.

Mac had never imagined her husband, Duncan, as a hairstylist before, but she was more than willing to let me show him how to wash, cut and style her hair. Here's how *any man* can do the same beautiful thing for his girl:

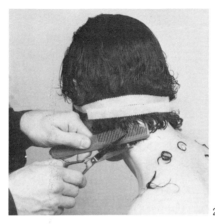

1 Wash, condition and towel-dry your girl's hair. Time for a quick cuddle, if you like – then comb it through.

2 Tape hair securely (two strips to hold that permed hair) across the back and use your comb to judge the cutting length. Hold it straight and cut underneath the comb. As you see, the hair is blunt-cut, not layered.

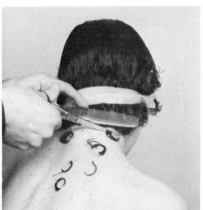

3 Continue cutting in small sections, checking the straight line as you do so. This should be repeated about every six weeks. The layers will gradually grow down and give an even look. If a long-haired lady attempts to grow it without cutting, she'll get a very tatty result which will be difficult to style.

4 Permed hair must be sectioned off to be blown dry. So, make a centre parting, then a horizontal one 2″ above the nape. Fix side hair securely away from your working area with clips.

5 Now, blow-dry using a good brush (like my Stylar model used by Duncan in the picture), flicking the curl down and then upwards. Continue blow-drying the layers, ending with the crown hair.

6 Use your fingers and the brush to shape the finished style. Togetherness is a hair-do for two. By the way, it's Duncan's turn next – those curls are definitely due for a trim.

20 Today's Lady with Today's Hair

To my mind there is no age limit to successful hairstyling. Today, haircutting, colouring and perming techniques depend entirely on the result you want, the condition of your hair and the life you lead.

Just because you're over fifty, you don't have to have a perm, roller-set and lots of lacquer – blow-drying or tonging can be much softer and more becoming. I advise women over forty to start taking *extra* care of the condition of their hair (naturally, all women, men and children should care about condition too – but later, the body becomes less able to 'fight back' once you've bombarded it with abuse, including heavy-handed hairdressing).

Here are five essential tips

1 Avoid having perm after perm – and be sure that the hairdresser cuts off all the old perm before re-doing it.
2 Avoid heavy handling – heated rollers, lots of lacquer, pins, grips, tight-fitting hats, scratchy brushes.
3 Increase good, high-protein foods and fresh fruits and vegetables in your diet.
4 Watch for falling hair, dandruff and lank, lifeless hair – which could be caused by bodily hormonal changes and be successfully treated by a doctor.
5 Choose the colour and style that fits in with your mode of life.

Jane, an elegant granny, is a friend of mine with fine hair, tending to dryness. She finds that the use of heavy conditioners makes it too soft and flat-looking and her experiments with blow-drying have not been successful since she had it cut short some time back. Although her hair is now naturally grey, she doesn't want to darken it as she feels this would be hard and ageing. So, she has highlights to soften the grey and needs a regular body perm to give height and width and to hold a style.

As you can see, there is quite a lot going on. I feel that a body perm and highlights is a combination that's doomed from the start (and was probably contributing to her dryness and handling problems). Why? Because highlights are put in with *bleach*. Now, you need a different perm lotion for bleached hair than you do for virgin hair, so how do you decide which one to use? Difficult!

Here's my solution to Jane's problem

She needed naturalizing, not highlighting. Naturalizing is simply a technique of placing streaks in the hair using one or more tint shades. Of course, it limits the amount of lightening that can be done, but is a much gentler and subtler technique. It also leaves the hair in good condition for a perm. On Jane's hair, a three-shade 'pepper and salt' effect looked very attractive.

I cut her hair into shape and tonged it into the soft style you see. This gave

fullness and softness – no hard edges to the style. I also advise her now to use a lighter conditioner and make sure all her old bleached highlights have disappeared before her next body perm.

Jane's make-up

Eyes are so important for all women – but especially for older ones. They often ignore eye make up altogether or apply it harshly, inadvertently adding years. On Jane, our make-up adviser applied a very fine foundation-base product to cover the whole of her face. A thicker make-up is no use for older women – it simply clogs in the wrinkles and looks terrible. She powdered over with a fine, translucent powder, avoiding too much around the eyes. Then, she set to work on the eyes:

1 and 2 Brows should be brushed neatly into shape. A soft creamy shadow or powder should be used, applied with a brush. Cream is kindest to dryish eyelids – but don't choose a pearly shadow, it looks hard and unnatural. For Jane, a cream-coloured shadow over the entire eyelid area, then soft brown on the outer lid only blended in to look soft.

3 Using a sharp, soft pencil, make a dark line around the eye. Soften this line, using a brush.

4 Then apply mascara (soft brown) to top and bottom lashes. If your lashes are very sparse, use fine 'falsies' – but practise with them first!

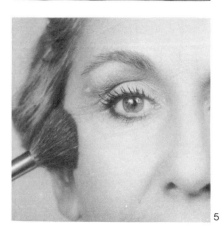

5 Use a tawny blusher high on the cheek-bones, softly blended in.

6 Choose a warm lip colour – not too dark or too bright. If your lips are wrinkly, don't use gloss. Apply lip colour with a brush for a neat outline, then fill in.

21 Your Make-up and Your Hairstyle

However brilliant your hairstyle, you need make-up to complement it. Even if you favour the natural look, you can look more naturally lovely with clever make-up. I'm always surprised by the number of women who spend pounds on their hair-do and yet never up-date their make-up. The two should go hand-in-hand, and the hairdresser's salon is often the best place to re-appraise your make-up and consider a new approach. If you have a new colour tint or a different style, then you must re-think your eye make-up and lip colour to give a total look.

Tone is all important for this total approach to beauty. If you have hair lightened, streaked or naturalized, then your eye make-up will probably need softening and lip-colour adjusting. Avoid hard shades if you're over forty — black liner and mascara with copper-coloured hair, for instance.

You are your own best make-up expert because you are familiar with the 'raw material' — your face. But when your hairstyle is new it takes a little while — and much experimentation — to get a new make-up look together. Practise until you can put on your daytime make-up quickly and expertly with the minimum of fuss.

In the evening, tone softens and lighting changes dramatically. Strengthen your daytime make-up with extra blusher, deeper shadow, more mascara. If you don't have time for a complete change of make-up, simply wipe your face gently with a tissue and apply more base, blusher, shadow. Remember that a small amount of a very dark colour can be softer and more effective than an abundance of a pale blue or green. Your make-up will last longer if it is gently powdered over with translucent loose powder. When it comes to removing make-up at night, do be thorough. Don't allow loose bits of powder and base to cling to your hairline — they could make your hair extra greasy. Pay particular attention to these areas when you're shampooing.

Fashion in make-up changes very subtly — if you let it! Don't be ensnared by the latest glittery lipstick if it just isn't you. Watch instead for changes of emphasis — deeper lips, paler shadows, softer colours. If you desperately need a total re-think, then it pays to go to a salon for a professional make-up lesson, after you've had your new hair-do cut and styled, naturally.

One important area to watch — your eyebrows. Lately, the heavier brow has become more fashionable. Which doesn't mean the shaggy look. Tidy brows make a tidy, chic face so do check that yours don't straggle, especially if you wear your hair in a fringe or front-swept style where the shaggy look could be just messy. Alternatively, be careful not to over-pluck your eyebrows, making them pencil thin. And if you lighten your hair, don't forget that the eyebrows should blend in with the new colour.

Check that your nails are well manicured — especially if you pat or fiddle with your hair a lot. Nails are noticed!

Organization is the winning word when it comes to looking good. Keep your make-up drawer tidy and organized, together with your hair-care equipment. Ruthlessly throw away old items which you'll never use again, and treat yourself to a pretty, inexpensive make-up purse every couple of months — not just when the old one falls to pieces. If you travel a lot, keep a whole duplicate make-up kit ready for instant use. Have a 'tidy' session one evening a week — wash out make-up bag, wash combs and brushes and throw away 'nasties'. Combine it with hair washing, manicuring and a lovely beauty bath — a total beauty night for the total look.

22 Your Bearded Wonder

Beards need gentle handling, careful cultivation and skilful cutting. I should know — I've worn one for four years.

The perfect beard looks trim and feels soft to the touch. This last bit is vital — ask the woman in your life, if you don't believe me.

What makes a beard prickly? Cutting it with an electric razor or clippers gives a flat edge to each hair, making a prickly effect. If you trim your beard with scissors (very sharp, naturally), then the cut angle of each hair is slanting, making the finished beard feel soft and silky.

When you decide to grow a beard, try not to look at yourself too often during the first, itchy stages. Keep calm and cool by splashing on cologne frequently — most men choose a holiday period for the first, difficult bit. Once enough hair has appeared to judge, take a long cool look at your hair, face shape and beard in the mirror. The beard should *balance* your hairstyle and face. This is the stage when a hairdresser's advice on styling the beard would be helpful. Make sure the beard balances your figure too — long whiskers on a short man could give the impression that he's continually about to get trapped under a bus.

Shampoo your beard every time you wash your hair and lather it with soap in the shower at least once a day. Otherwise, it will soon become itchy and uncomfortable. Trim it yourself regularly, or get the beard-fancier in your life to do it for you!

My friend Colin is a 'regular' at the Debenham's gym where I go for my daily exercise. He has strong, fairly curly hair and when we first met he was having a big problem controlling it. It was neither long nor short, but managing to develop rather too much curl for a neat look. It now looks smart worn fairly short. Here's my step-by-step guide for beard and moustache trimming using Colin as a model:

You need
shampoo, conditioner, towel
sharp scissors
comb
mirror.

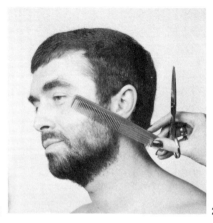

1 Shampoo and condition hair (under the shower if you like) and towel-dry hair lightly. Leave beard damp.

2 Comb beard through first to untangle any knots, combing in a downward direction.

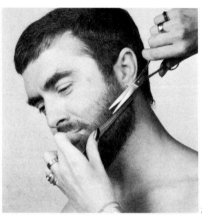

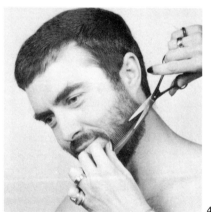

3 Place your comb against the hair, teeth pointing upwards. Now lightly press comb against the face and trim away the beard sticking through the comb. In small sections, naturally. Your scissors must be super-sharp.

4 Continue all over the beard, combing as you cut. Although Colin asked a girlfriend to trim his beard for him, you can easily do this yourself. In fact, this is how I cut my own beard, unless one of my colleagues does it for me.

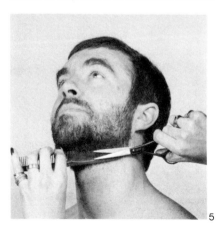

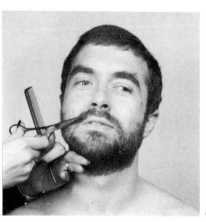

5 Careful under his chin! You must use a steady hand – if he says it tickles, stop for a moment!

6 Place one hand on his chin, and lean your scissors-hand against it to steady you, especially around that delicate lip area. Comb through, and trim neatly.

23 The Products You Need

In the last few years, the number of hair-care products on the market has increased enormously. This is often very confusing indeed for the general public, faced with massive advertising and shelf upon shelf piled high with the 'latest and greatest' shampoos, conditioners and specialist treatment products.

Often, I've found that clients have been using the wrong products for their particular hair type at home – with disastrous results. It can be an expensive business to experiment with different shampoos, conditioners and creams until you find the 'perfect' products for your own hair. What's more, your hair isn't constantly in a stable condition, so that the super conditioning shampoo you bought last week may be far too greasy for your hair this week.

How can you save time and money by choosing the right products? First, know your hair and your body! If your hair sometimes goes greasy when you're under pressure, make note of the fact and stock up with a good dry shampoo. If your normally greasy hair dries up in hot sunshine, take a milder, gentler shampoo with you on holiday than you usually use. Get to know your hair and its moods. Second, read the information on the product packaging before you buy it. There may be four identical green hair sprays on the shelf – don't just grab one, look closer to see if they're meant for different types of hair. Otherwise you could end up with the wrong type. Just because one manufacturer's lemon-based shampoo is for greasy hair, don't assume that all lemon shampoos are fine for greasy hair. Maybe the one you choose will be a lemon, honey and rum concoction meant for dry hair. Third, read the manufacturer's instructions thoroughly before using the product. The biggest single cause of hair disasters in my experience is incorrect use of a product – which may have been the wrong product in the first place. Fourth, watch the magazines and newspapers for advertisements and editorial recommendations. This will keep you up to date on new items which could help your hair-care programme.

I've worked with all the big-name hair preparations and I've found that particular firms are strong on certain items. Redken, for instance, make a superb cream conditioning rinse (Phinal Phase), and Schwarzkopf make the best dry shampoo for greasy hair (Batiste) I've found anywhere. Here's my guide to just a few of these firms with their ranges of excellent products – several are right for *you*.

Redken is a California-based company which now has outlets in this country and around the world. They specialize in scientifically formulated hair-care products which emphasize the importance of PH (the acid balance so often disturbed by harsh shampoos and soaps), protein and natural organic ingredients.

The products are carefully grouped to treat various hair problems – from frizziness to excessive oiliness. But, the Redken philosophy insists that their products should be used by trained stylists. Most Redken salons sell products direct to customers – and some sell their excellent skin-care range too. Don't confuse the two, although all the shampoos and conditioners are good for your hands.

Amino Pon Shampoo – acid-balanced organic shampoo, with a special non-colour stripping formula which makes it safe on tinted hair. *Airset Heat Styling Lotion* – this is a protective lotion to use on your hair *before* styling with hot combs, heated rollers, tongs and other gadgets which can dry and ruin your hair. *Phinal Phase Creme Rinse* – super conditioning rinse, acid-balanced to leave hair shining and manageable. *Climatress Moisturising Creme Protein Conditioner* – a great conditioner for dry, brittle hair, minimizes colour fading and helps a set last longer. *Amino Pon Deep Cleansing Shampoo* – for really deep cleansing when hair is very dirty or greasy.

Wella has been established for nearly a hundred years, and now operates in 130 countries throughout the world. Their head office, laboratories and superb Hair Museum are situated at Darmstadt, West Germany. Salon stylists know their colouring, permanent waving and conditioning products well. I'm a great fan of their men's range and the new Wella Care range of gentle, thorough hair conditioning products.

The Wella Care range – Almond shampoo for dry hair (leaves it soft and easy to comb through), Lemon shampoo for greasy hair, Herbal shampoo for normal hair. Almond, Lemon and Herbal Spray Sets – all to spray on your hair just before or after rolling up. Almond, Lemon and Herbal Balsam Creme Rinse – cream rinses for dry, greasy and normal hair types respectively, should be used after every shampoo to maintain hair in top condition.

Wella Hair Spray – comes in normal and hard-to-hold types. *Body N' Bounce* is a conditioning hair set for fine, fly-away hair. *Blo Dry Lotion* is applied to hair after shampooing and before blow-drying to make hair easier to handle and style (excellent, I think). *Hair Set* – a good lotion to use before roller-setting. *Conditioner* – specially formulated to penetrate, nourish and strengthen damaged, split and over-treated hair.

Wella For Men – a *Regular* and *Anti-dandruff Shampoo*, *Conditioner* and a regular and medicated liquid *Hairdressing* to stimulate the scalp. In addition, there is a *Spray Dressing* to control hair.

Clairol is a top American company, really expert on colourants and hair-conditioning preparations. I suggest anyone with hard-to-style hair has a splurge on a sachet of one of Clairol's Natural Balance conditioners.

Natural Balance conditioners (bottle or single-application sachets), for dry or brittle hair, fine or fly-away hair, normal or greasy hair. *Quiet Touch* is a new concept in streaking – it's simply painted on dry hair. Effective for mousy, fairish hair, not so successful on darker heads. *Nice 'n Easy* is the biggest-selling hair colourant on the market. *Born Blonde* is an excellent range of lighteners with lotion toners for a two-step blonding process; recommended for home-tinted blondes, but use with great care, following the directions. *Loving Care* is a semi-permanent colourant for greying hair. Clairol also make *Crazy Curl*, a super steam styling wand to make curls just where you want them; *Crazy Curl 'n Shape* with brush attachment; the *De Luxe 3-Way Hairsetter*, consisting of twenty heated rollers and conditioner; and the *3-Way Hairsetter* with sixteen heated rollers.

Carmen revolutionized hair care with their heated rollers – unbelievably only twelve years ago. Now they have much more sophisticated roller sets and other beauty products too – I recommend the Cascade set with built-in conditioner.

Carmen Cascade Curlers – use them with or without conditioner which is poured into the set, and forms a conditioning film over the rollers while they heat up – they're then used on dry hair. Ideal on holiday when hair tends to be dried by the sun and sea.

Henna (Hair Health) Ltd came onto the hair care scene in 1974 with products based on the red henna powder made from the dried leaves of the Egyptian Privet used to condition and colour hair down the centuries. As well as revamping the original red powder, they also make super treatment products which do not alter the colour of the hair. I'm impressed by their treatment shampoos and their excellent Treatment Wax.

Henna Lifeplus Balsam – a highly active hair conditioner for dry, dull and damaged hair. *Henna Herbal Shampoo* – gentle but thorough shampoo for normal and greasy hair. *Henna Treatment Wax* – this is a hair food conditioner formulated with vegetable henna. Use it on dry, over-bleached, permed and dull hair. It is also excellent for Afro-type hair and should be used in conjunction with hot towels. I recommend applying the wax, covering the hair with transparent food wrap, then a hot towel, perhaps while you're in the bath.

Henna Powder – comes in Natural Red, Brown and Golden shades. Henna (Hair Health) Ltd have just introduced three new powders: Black – for brunettes with medium brown to black hair achieves a translucent effect, brightens and polishes; Chestnut Brown creates glowing chestnut tones when used on light to medium brown hair; Dark Warm Brown, as its name implies, is ideal for medium to dark brown hair when rich and warm dark brown tones result. Use the Brown and Golden on all shades of naturally brown and mousy hair to feed and nourish the hair and add warmth and shine to the colour. The Natural Red shade gives red tints to medium or dark hair. All are safe to use on tinted or permed hair.

Henna Gloss Shampoo for Brunettes – enhances and conditions natural brown or tinted brown hair, and nourishes and feeds damaged hair too. *Gloss Shampoo for Redheads* is also available. *Golden Highlights Vegetable Creme Colour* – natural cream henna which adds golden red highlights to light brown, mousy or medium brown hair.

Schwarzkopf is a long-established German hair care company with divisions all over the world. Most leading salons use their excellent colouring and conditioning products. Recently, they brought out a range called Batiste, especially for controlling greasy hair. Look for it in green packaging on the hair care counters.

The Batiste range – Shampoo, specially formulated to remove excessive oil gently, comes in three sizes. Creme rinse – this is applied after washing your hair to help slow down grease build-up and balance the condition; comes in two sizes. Spray set – aerosol spray to make your set last longer after or between shampooing. Hair Spray – holds hair and helps control greasy hair. Dry shampoo – delicious smelling spray shampoo – spray on and brush out between normal, wet shampoos.

The Paletta range is for normal hair. Colour Set – a product which comes in a range of colours and is used as a brightener for your existing colour (which is perhaps fading a little) or as a toner for harshness caused by 'lifting' in sunshine. Hair Set – in Normal Hold and Extra Hold strengths for setting your style. Roller set – a spray-on lotion to use before winding up rollers. Blow Dry – another spray-on lotion, this time to use before blow-drying your style.

The Corimist range is for dry hair. Each preparation contains conditioners to cope with this problem. Firm Hold Hair Spray, Regular Care Creme Rinse, Deep Care Conditioner, Firm Hold Hair Set, Shampoo and Quick-Set are self-explanatory. Spray Tonic is a good product – you simply spray it on to help your hair look prettier, softer for longer – super if it's the 'bird's nest' type!

Haffenden Richborough market some of the best hairstyling tools you can buy – under the Harold Leighton label! Seriously, they've been designed by yours truly to answer all the needs of hairstyling and they really do make blow-drying and styling your own hair a simple, professional operation instead of a hit-and-miss affair. I'm continually adding to the range as I feel specific needs arrive in the hairdressing field – needs which are dictated by fashion, changing trends in living, working, travelling. Watch this space (and your local stockist) for further developments!